THE BATTLE FOR
BALANCE

How to win life by aligning your
wellbeing, work and **world**

SIMON SHEPARD

Re think

First published in Great Britain in 2021
by Rethink Press (www.rethinkpress.com)

Cover image © Adobe/Olga Lyubkin

Contents

Preface   1

Introduction   3

Knowledge versus actions   5

Machines versus humans   5

Being versus doing   6

Scoring your goals   8

SECTION 1 The Theory   11

1 Wellbeing, Performance And Resilience   15

The skill of resilience   16

Step 1 – Recognition   19

Step 2 – Reframe, release, learn   23

Step 3 – Reset   25

Step 4 – Respond and react   29

2 Stress   **31**

What is stress?   32

The physiology of stress   35

Stress in excess   36

Excessive stress and the body   38

Excessive stress and the brain   40

Measuring stress   41

SECTION 2 The First Goal: You And Your Wellbeing   **47**

3 Understanding Yourself   **51**

Sleep   55

Exercise   67

Nutrition   71

4 Creating Your Plan   **77**

Goals: From SMART to SMARTIES   78

Emotional attachment   80

Ask for help   81

Accountability   82

SECTION 3 The Second Goal: You And Your Work   **87**

5 Leading In The Twenty-First Century   **91**

Understanding   92

Balance 93

Adaptability 95

Consequence analysis 97

Adaptive communication 100

6 Motivation 105

The CRAFT of motivation 106

Take a holistic approach to appraisals 111

Stop wasting time 114

Creating a time-effective culture 121

Values and Mission 122

Culture and anti-culture 126

SECTION 4 The Third Goal: You And Your World 133

7 What Is A Community? 137

Community giving 138

Community supporting 139

Community being 140

A community is complex 143

Community architecture 147

8 Dismantling Barriers 153

Generational angst 153

Intellectual inertia 159

Conclusion   165

Further Reading   169

Acknowledgements   173

The Author   177

Preface

I started writing this book in December 2019 when the world was approaching the dawn of a new decade. In the UK, the policy of austerity was starting to lessen, Brexit appeared to be reaching a point of resolution, and there was an inkling of hope that 2020 would live up to its name and be a time for clarity of vision.

As I finish, the positive dreams have been shattered and replaced by a nightmare of destruction and disease. The extreme bushfires that wreaked havoc in Australia were simply a prelude for a pandemic that has impacted the human race to such an extent, the world seems to be more muddled than ever. The environment has been damaged, businesses drained and many people have been left devastated. If ever there was a time to reset and think about how we are playing the game of life, it is now.

The Battle for Balance is neither an academic tome, nor a blueprint for how to lead your life. Instead it is a reflection on some of the experiences, learnings and conversations I have had through my career in health, sport and business; encounters that have shaped my thoughts on the way the world is going round at an individual, corporate and community level. I hope the ideas in this book will encourage you to think about how you are living, move away from the generic messages that to many seem to have little effect, get creative and take ownership of the way you interact with life.

Introduction

I have been incredibly lucky in my career. Day in, day out, people have let me into their worlds. As a physiotherapist, patients have consented to me examining their aches and pains; working in sport has allowed me to sit in the inner sanctum of a professional dressing room and witness how a team may sink or swim; while corporate organisations have trusted me to wire up their staff with technology and talk to them about their energy, focus and purpose. In every domain, I am afforded a privileged understanding into the way people think and function.

While some individuals are unquestionably 'winning', there are a significant number who are finding that everyday life can be tough. Their health may be challenged; their teams may fail to perform; their businesses may struggle to deal with the accelerated changes that the working world of the twenty-first century demands.

The commonly bandied about yet poorly understood phrase 'quality of life' can be described as 'living a life that is closely aligned to what is important to you at any given time'. This highlights that it is both personal – what makes you tick may not have an iota of relevance to your neighbour – and timely – what is important to you today may be the least of your concerns next week – but the key word is 'aligned', and this theme is at the heart of this book.

How aligned are you with yourself, your work and your community?

With the spotlight increasingly on poor mental health, it appears that many of us are finding the turbulence of life to be unsettling. Challenges are thrown at us by colleagues, friends, family and, indeed, ourselves. The acronym VUCA (volatility, uncertainty, complexity and ambiguity) is highly relevant in today's world; we become misaligned as events overwhelm us, and rather than taking control of life, we may find that life starts to take control of us. Fractures appear, and before we know it, our energy, focus and purpose can dissolve and disappear.

I typically refer to the factors that start this erosion as 'the disconnects' and they tend to fall into one of three categories:

Knowledge versus actions

Many people have a desire to be healthy, but despite knowing that good nutrition, exercise and sleep are all likely to contribute to their wish, they embark on a lifestyle that is totally contrary to this. In other words, they know what they should do, but find it hard to do it.

For example, imagine you are attending a conference with a long day of networking ahead, an event that is important for your business. You have stayed at a hotel close by, and in the morning, you walk down for breakfast and are greeted with an array of choices. The fry-up is not the healthy option, there are other options that are more likely to keep you energised throughout the day, but the likelihood is, you just can't resist. The disconnect between knowledge and actions may result not just in poor health but also in poor business.

Machines versus humans

With the numerous online platforms that allow us to communicate with ferocious regularity, the speed and functionality of technology are growing at an exponential rate. To highlight this, Forbes showed that between 2000 and 2009 the number of emails sent globally increased from 12 billion to 247 billion per day,[1] while the *Wall Street Journal* reports that as of June 2020 there were over 50 million users of WhatsApp Business.[2] Considering this service has only been in existence since 2018 that is quite some growth. There is no sign of digital communication nor its accompanying artificial intelligence slowing down, but has this always added to our productivity? I suspect not, and it is highly likely that the disconnect between the capability of machines and humans will continue to widen.

Being versus doing

As a species, we are known as human beings, yet much of our time is simply spent addressing the drudgery of day-to-day life and we fail to spend any time thinking or interacting with what we consider to be important. Author of *The 7 Habits of Highly Successful People*,[3] Stephen Covey, highlights the importance of 'putting first things first'. People often state that their wellbeing and their relationships are important, but

1 Oliver J Chiang, 'The Decade In Data', *Forbes*, 2009. www.forbes.com/2009/12/27/broadband-text-messages-technology-cio-network-data

2 Dave Sebastian, 'WhatsApp's Business-User Base Grew Tenfold From 2019', *Wall Street Journal*, 2020. www.wsj.com/articles/whatsapps-business-user-base-grew-tenfold-from-2019-11594298961

3 Stephen Covey, *The 7 Habits of Highly Effective People: Powerful lessons in personal change* (The Free Press, 2004)

they then let the other things in life dominate. This is a good example of a disconnect between actions and stated priorities.

The Battle For Balance is a book that aims to make you aware of these voids, encourage you to resolve the disconnects and create a stronger bond between your purpose and your actions.

Before we start, though, it will be useful for you to think about why you want to play the game and how you want to play it. What is your big picture? What is truly important to you? Where does your heart belong? What are your drivers in life?

It could be that you are interested in happiness, money, security, title, wellbeing, longevity of life. There will be plenty of possibilities and there is no right or wrong. I simply encourage you to make sure that you are being true to yourself – that the answer is yours rather than echoing your partner's, parents', friends' or even that of some form of alter-ego you may have.

Once you are clear on why you are playing the game, think about your foundation stones – what are the non-negotiable values that underpin your personal identity? You will need to think long and hard, and may have to talk to those who know you well to reveal these values and determine how you are going to play the game of life.

By way of an example, I am going to share with you some of the things that are important to me at this moment in time. Currently, I am driven by financial stability, travelling less than I have done over the past decade and being respected by my professional peers. This is why I want to play the game – if I achieve these things, I will feel energised.

And the rules I want to play by are:

- Fairness – both to myself and others

- Be progressive – always be ahead of the curve

- Community – create mutual benefit

Living a values-driven life is likely to make you tick. Equally, if there is something nagging away in the back of your mind, you will often find that you're not playing the game in a way that sits comfortably with you. The problem can sometimes be external, but in many cases, you will find that you have deviated away from your own rule book and *you* are the source of the trouble.

Scoring your goals

'An apple a day keeps the doctor away' is a generic proverb that, while full of good intention, is not always the soundest advice, especially if you are allergic to apples. In the same way, this book is not a set formula. Rather, it features a range of ingredients, some that you will already use, some that are just not for you and others you may consider experimenting with. While you potentially have three goals to score, the good news is there are many ways in which you can score them.

The first goal relates to looking after yourself. It explores how you can create the physical, mental and emotional energy to live with a sense of personal purpose.

The second goal relates to being focused and effective, especially in your world of work. It will challenge you to reflect on not just what you do, but how and why you do it.

The third goal encourages the concept of community. This is a word that people often gravitate towards, but what does it really mean to you? How are you going to interact with your community?

Your task is to find the ingredients that work for you and blend them into a recipe that puts a smile on your face. Remember that what is right for others is not necessarily right for you, while respecting that what is right for you may not be right for others.

Make things personal!

SECTION 1
THE THEORY

Wellbeing, resilience and performance are words that feature throughout this book. But as they are often interpreted in a number of ways, it is hardly surprising that there can be some confusion as to what they actually mean. Like many other words, they just come out of our mouths with little thought for what we are talking about, and the result is white noise. Try asking your friends what stress is, or your colleagues to define wellbeing, and you will soon hear the inconsistencies and variation.

With apologies, before we get into the excitement of scoring goals, we need to take a look at both language and theory to ensure we have a common understanding of what lies ahead.

1
Wellbeing, Performance And Resilience

With descriptions varying from the clinical 'a good or satisfactory state of existence'[4] to the rather more human 'a state of feeling healthy and happy',[5] the word **wellbeing** can be confusing. I often suggest that it can be summarised by the single word 'content'. This is a word that describes a state of inner peace. If we have this, we have achieved wellbeing.

Traditionally, wellbeing was associated with physical health, but more recently, people have increasingly accepted that it goes way further, evaluating how content they feel from an intellectual, emotional and

---

4   'Wellbeing' definition, Dictionary.com. www.dictionary.com/browse/well-being
5   'Wellbeing' definition, Cambridge dictionary. https://dictionary.cambridge.org/dictionary/english/well-being

spiritual standpoint. It can also be helpful to ask how content we are with work, friendships, finances, environment, self and life in general.

Typically relating to a task, **performance** can be described as our output in relation to what we set out to achieve. We all tend to aim for good performance, so it is a word that tends to be associated with the positive. But performance does not equal excellence, and we need to acknowledge that poor, bad or indifferent versions can exist. As such, it is a word that requires some qualification.

Resilience is a word that has become increasingly popular over the past decade; so much so that it is now a much sought-after trait. Defined as the ability to deal with difficulties quickly, it relates to both impact and time. It is also something that can be broken down into a skill.

The skill of resilience

Human beings crave stability, yet we have created a world that changes at an incredible pace. Accompanying the never-ending state of external flux is the growth of media platforms, meaning that our exposure is conscious, instantaneous and continuous. This environment makes us part of the disruption, so our need for resilience has become increasingly important.

Before we look at how to develop the skill of resilience, there are two important points to consider. First, resilience does not equal robustness. The robust person is the one who constantly says yes: 'Yes, I'll do it', 'Yes, it's not a problem', 'Yes, leave it there and I will sort it out'. They are the dependable, loyal, trusty servant who, along with a never-empty in-tray, has a total inability to say no. They just keep taking on more and more.

If you are like this and you see changes in how you are feeling or your energy levels are flagging, please do something to address the situation. When the robust person breaks, whether it be in health, performance or both, the break is often big. The Japanese even have a word that describes the most serious consequence, *karoshi* means death through overwork.

With the increasing incidence of burnout around the world, it would seem that either the number of robust people is decreasing or our ability to spot and support the robust person is diminishing, or – and I suspect this is most likely – it is a combination of the two.

The second point is that resilience is not just about the world changing around us; it is also about how we adapt in our world. This story makes the point well.

My children, at the ages of twenty-four and twenty-one, have mastered the skill of drinking a glass of water, but when they were much younger, this was not the case. As a family, we would sit down for a meal in the evening and one of them would invariably spill their water. Typically, I would get a cloth, wipe up the mess, refill the glass and sit down to carry on enjoying the family meal. Occasionally, though, my reaction would be totally different. The time of day, location, people, occurrence would be the same; the only thing that had changed was me.

It is important to remember that resilience is a two-way street and that the easier side of the street to control is our own side.

The skills associated with resilience are often seen in sport where people put much time and effort into ensuring optimal physical recovery. Hydration, nutrition, stretching, massage, ice baths and good-quality sleep are all important, but for those sportspeople who achieve sustained success, psychological resilience tends to be a dominant trait. They will have processes to deal with injury, loss of form and the pressures of fame and fortune. Sometimes, the processes will not follow the textbook – meditation is not for everyone; however, these individuals will have worked out a way to ensure that when the pressure is on, they are emotionally grounded.

Too many people, and indeed businesses as a whole, think that resilience just happens. It doesn't. While some may appear to find dealing with the demands of day-to-day life easier than others, their resilience is a skill they have practised. And when it's broken down into a series of steps, it can be practised by all.

Step 1 – Recognition

If you do not create the occasional moment to stop and ask yourself 'How am I doing?' and 'Why am I feeling like this?', then you are leaving the skill of resilience to chance. Recognition is key, yet it is something that people often neglect. In fact, many seem to be far better at inspecting and offering an opinion on how other people are doing in life than thinking about themselves.

There are many ways to formalise recognition. Some are straightforward while others require more time and effort. If you want to keep things really simple, you could do a weekly check-in and give yourself a score out of ten as to how content you feel. If you want to inspect your resilience in a bit more depth, then you might find the Focus Energy Matrix useful. First proposed by Bruch and Ghoshal,[6] this tool looks at the relationship between these two key factors and can be expanded to open up a narrative around how you have been functioning. I have modified a couple of the words in the model: where the original authors used 'distraction', I prefer the word 'chaos', and 'disengagement' has been replaced by 'fatigue'.

---

6   Heike Bruch and Sumantra Ghoshal, 'Beware The Busy Manager', *Harvard Business Review*, 2002. https://hbr.org/2002/02/beware-the-busy-manager

The process involves thinking about what percentage of time you have spent being purposeful, chaotic, procrastinating or feeling fatigued, and placing a number in each of the quadrants – the total needs to add up to 100%. You may want to put in two sets of scores, one for life at work and one for life away from it, as they are rarely the same.

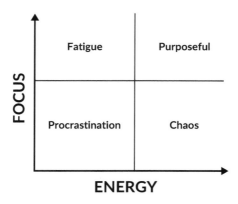

Modified Focus Energy Quadrant 'In The Zone'

- **Purposeful** is the sweet spot when high energy is matched with high focus.

- **Chaos** is when there is plenty of energy, but focus is low. You're spinning plates, juggling balls and multitasking.

- **Procrastination** reflects the time when you're not getting much done. This quadrant can be interpreted in a couple of ways. If low energy and low focus are leading to paralysis, this is clearly negative. If the quadrant has been used to reset for a moment, then that is positive. You may find it helpful to place two numbers, representing the positive and negative, in this box.

- **Fatigue** is when you know what needs to be done, but simply do not have the energy to do it. If fatigue is ignored, then burnout is a distinct possibility.

Once you have the scores in place, you will understand what has been going on in your life, but to use this tool effectively, you also need to think about the commentary that sits behind the numbers. What is the why behind them?

If your purpose is high and you have had a great month, think about the factors that have allowed you to be so effective and write them down. It is common for people to perform detailed analysis when things are not going so well, looking at problems from every angle, but I find it astounding how little reflection and evaluation takes place during times of success. Understand what sits behind the good and create a template for replication.

If the chaos percentage is high, it is worth examining why you are functioning so inefficiently. Is it due to a lack of knowledge? This may mean you have to focus on learning. Is it due to an external factor, something that is impossible to influence? In this case, you need to harness the skill of release (see Step 2). Could it be down to poor communication, resulting in one part of the team working towards one objective while another is heading in a totally different direction? Once you know the why, you can address the problem head on.

If the procrastination percentage is high, what is at the root of this state? The source could again be a practical factor such as an absence of knowledge or funding, or the block could be triggered by previous experiences that so often create a reduction in self-esteem, belief and confidence.

If the fatigue percentage is high, address it. Ignoring this can lead to mistakes, poor health, resignation, 'fed-up-itis' or a fusion of all four. Either way, there are few winners, and rates of absence or attrition are likely to be high.

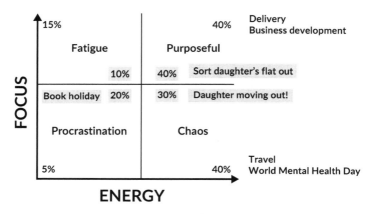

Completed 'In The Zone'; shaded numbers and wording reflect life away from work, unshaded numbers and words reflect life at work

When you use this model, two tips may help. First, if the chaos score is increasing, you need to act. If you do not, I am afraid there is only one place you are heading, and that is to the fatigue quadrant.

Second, it is hard to jump from chaos to purposeful. Learn how to introduce a moment of reset, which is something we will cover later in this chapter.

Step 2 – Reframe, release, learn

Many people describe stress as being out of control. Their negative mindset takes over and their progress is surrounded by barriers. Their dialogue will be heavily populated with words that end with 'n't' – can't, shouldn't, haven't and won't – along with other negative words such as 'impossible'.

Reframing is all about taking back control of a situation and learning to use language that gets rid of the n'ts. It is not as simple as just changing can't to can; for example, I can't and never will be able to run a 100 m in under 10 seconds. The reframe has to be matched with realism.

Don't worry about it. Just let it go. Easily said, but following through and really **releasing** something that's been troubling you can be incredibly hard to do. Like so many things in life, though, the more you practise this, the more effective you will become.

It is important to be mindful of the sentiment behind needing to let something go. This could involve telling a friend or colleague how you feel; writing the challenge down on a piece of paper, then screwing it up and tossing it in the bin; going for a quick walk whenever the thought comes into your head. Whatever your strategy, make sure that you are deliberate in your approach.

It is incredible how few people remember that one of the most effective ways to deal with a challenge is to **learn**. A good example here involves IT. While some people are highly adept at navigating their way around the maze that technology places in front of them, others will struggle to tell the difference between their USB and their RAM. The machines that are designed to make their lives easier are actually doing totally the opposite. If we also recognise that technology is likely to advance at a far greater speed than people's mastery of IT (forgive the pun), the challenge is compounded and our resilience is tested.

Whether learning is formal or achieved through colleague support, take the time to align your knowledge with the task in hand. It is an investment that will save time and energy.

Step 3 – Reset

I am not an expert on motorsport, but occasionally, I will watch a Formula 1 race. The cars whizz round the track at ridiculous speeds, and every twenty laps or so, the driver stops and pulls into the pit lane, where the mechanics rapidly change tyres and refuel the car with finely tuned skills. Apparently, an incredible amount of thought goes into when the driver does this.

Why does the car come to a halt in the middle of a race? It seems counterintuitive.

The answer, of course, is that stopping provides the driver with the best chance to win. The mechanics recognise that taking a proactive approach to the performance of the vehicle, as opposed to continually pushing it to racing speed, will reap rewards.

If we as human beings can look after cars in this way, why is it that we rarely think about how we reset ourselves? Rather than taking control of the race we let our day-to-day races take control of us; we just keep on pushing until we break. Whether the reset be physical, nutritional, intellectual or emotional, it is an essential part of the resilience process.

Physical reset

Sitting for long periods is not good news. Aside from increasing the likelihood of back and neck pain, the lack of movement increases the risk of cardiovascular disease and type 2 diabetes.

Back pain is one of the biggest causes of absence from work. While continuous lifting can be a trigger, for many people, the real enemy is prolonged sitting. Sitting for as little as an hour will result in a reduction in the range of movement in the thoracic spine, the middle part of the spinal column sitting between the cervical (neck) and the lumbar (low back) regions.

While people will more often experience pain in the lumbar or cervical regions, their symptoms can often be triggered by stiffness in the thoracic vertebrae. Simply making a habit of getting up from your desk every hour, walking around, shrugging your shoulders, twisting from side to side and taking a couple of deep breaths can restore some thoracic mobility.

Nutritional reset

Put simply, we need energy and fluids to function effectively. If a job is physical, we will need calories (ideally healthy ones), so ensuring that we top up regularly is important. Dehydration levels of as little as 2% will have a negative impact on mental productivity so it is equally important we respect the need for fluids.

Intellectual reset

At the start of the day, many people are good at thinking about what they need to get done. In fact, they are often so good, they enhance their clarity by collating these thoughts into a to-do list.

The trouble is, things change. It could be that a colleague is off sick, a meeting is cancelled, a contract is lost, the school rings to say that a child is unwell and needs to be taken home. Suddenly, the to-do list has flown out of the window.

Put this alongside the suggestion that the productivity level of human beings drops after less than an hour's intellectual activity[7] and there may be some benefit in taking control on more occasions than just the start of the day. There are a variety of techniques that have been developed by time-management experts: Francesco Cirillo's Pomodoro method advocates twenty-five minutes' work then five minutes' rest,[8] while Andrew May recommends five minutes'

---

7   Derek Thompson, 'A Formula for Perfect Productivity: Work for 52 minutes, break for 17', *The Atlantic*, 2014. www.theatlantic.com/business/archive/2014/09/science-tells-you-how-many-minutes-should-you-take-a-break-for-work-17/380369

8   Francesco Cirillo, *The Pomodoro Method: The life-changing time management system* (Virgin Books, 2009)

planning, fifty minutes' doing, then five minutes' break time.[9]

These techniques can be highly beneficial and the choice is yours, but if you decide that working flat out for ten hours is going to be great for your productivity, you are likely to be wrong. The human brain needs to reset and refocus if it is going to be efficient.

Emotional reset

Our emotions can change quickly when we're stressed due to both an increase in the activity of the limbic system, the emotional centre of the brain, and a reduction in the coherence of the cerebral cortex, the grey matter that helps to regulate the appropriateness of an emotional response. We may say things we regret or write emails that come back to haunt us; we may become loud and extrovert, or withdraw into our shell, as stress impacts our thinking and behaviour.

One of the best ways to achieve emotional control is to create a moment of pause and not just breathe but breathe effectively. There are many timing patterns that you can try, but I typically breathe in for six seconds and out for eight seconds. The important thing is to ensure that the breath is controlled by the diaphragm muscle that sits at the base of your lungs. You'll know you're doing it correctly if your tummy

---

9   Andrew May website, www.andrewmay.com

moves in and out, rather than your shoulders rising up and down. This increases the amount of air that enters your lungs per breath, reducing activity in the limbic system and providing the reset you require for the cortex to function effectively.

Step 4 – Respond and react

The whole point of steps one to three is to allow you time to respond and react to a challenge in an effective manner. Remember, resilience is the ability to recover quickly from difficulties. You cannot get stuck in recognition or spend all day resetting; you will need to move through the steps at an appropriate pace. Be mindful of the process and deliberate with practice and you will create a better chance of fine-tuning a highly beneficial skill.

Before moving on to the thing that so often challenges our resilience, stress, I want to highlight that the skill of resilience has to be underpinned by strong foundation stones. Without good-quality sleep, exercise, nutrition, positive relationships and an understanding of what is important to you, your chances of becoming resilient will be greatly reduced, no matter how well you follow the process.

2
Stress

Marie Curie is quoted as saying: 'Nothing in life is to be feared, it is only to be understood. Now is the time to understand more, so that we may fear less.' A century later, her insight is highly pertinent to the phenomenon of stress – something that seems to be everywhere, impacting many and creating confusion, yet something that, so often, is misinterpreted.

According to statistics from the Health and Safety Executive, the United Kingdom sees 17.9 million working days a year lost due to stress, anxiety or depression.[10] Put this alongside a dramatic rise in the cost to business associated with workplace stress (Matrix suggests the increase across Europe to be

---

10   National Statistics, 'Work-related Stress, Anxiety or Depression Statistics in Great Britain', Health and Safety Executive, 2020. www. hse.gov.uk/statistics/causdis/stress.pdf

greater than 3,000% since the turn of the century)[11] and it is right to conclude that the impact is high. Add in a pandemic that sees people facing uncertainty over health, finances and even personal identity, it is fair to say that the problem is likely to worsen.

If stress is a personal challenge to you, gaining a greater understanding of the enemy is a good starting point in the battle against it.

What is stress?

If people are asked to define the word stress, they are often drawn towards the negatives. An inability to cope; being out of control, anxious and overloaded – these are typical of the words and phrases I hear repeatedly in this context. Equally, if they are asked how stress makes them feel, they offer a pessimistic dialogue of emotions and physical symptoms:

- Frustrated
- Angry
- Tearful
- Unhappy
- Hopeless

- Headache
- Unsettled stomach
- Exhausted
- Tense
- Spotty

---

11   Matrix, 'Economic analysis of workplace mental health promotion and mental disorder prevention programmes and of their potential contribution to EU health, social and economic policy objectives', Executive Agency for Health and Consumers, 2013. http:// ec.europa.eu/health/mental_health/docs/matrix_economic_ analysis_mh_promotion_en.pdf

If people are asked how excessive stress impacts their day-to-day behaviour, many will acknowledge that it can trigger a deviation away from their norm. Some people become louder and more extrovert, others become quieter and introversion will dominate; some people will eat more, others will eat less; and for many, there is greater interaction with and dependence on alcohol, recreational drugs or other forms of addictive behaviour.

These shifts in behaviour are important to recognise as not only can changes be detrimental to the individual, they can also be damaging for relationships. Friendships are often built on typical behaviours which, if altered, can place strain on the social bonds that keep people together. Some relationships are quite trivial, but there are others when a breakdown can have deeper consequences.

And, of course, the most important relationship that can be placed under duress is the one with ourselves. Many people find it hard to be nice to themselves when they're stressed. It is a shame that the word 'nice' is ridiculed for its softness; if more people abided by this basic principle in every dimension, I suspect the world would be a happier place. 'Just be nice' is a great mantra to consider.

With the possibility of damage to health, performance, relationships and the simple ability to look after ourselves, it is hardly surprising that stress is often thought of in one way – as a catastrophe. But this view lacks balance as it is not always the case. If people – and it is often the same people who give the negative responses I listed earlier – are asked whether stress can be good, the majority are likely to suggest that the answer is yes. Not too much, of course, but they generally acknowledge that a certain degree of stress can be useful when it comes to functioning effectively in day-to-day life.

Both the negative and the positive views of stress are correct, but it is an interesting observation on human nature that the majority of people default to a negative position when confronted with the word. To help create a more balanced view, you may find it useful to think of stress as a response to a demand. The response could be good, it could be bad; it may be physical, psychological, emotional or behavioural; extreme or minimal. But it is simply a response to the load that is going through your body and brain at a moment in time.

Another concept for consideration is that of cause and effect. Too often, this is simplified: we assume that the same stressor will lead to the same response, but due to the complexity of human beings and our ever-changing moods, this doesn't happen.

For example, if you are stuck in a traffic jam, it may result in you ranting and raving, honking your horn and slapping the dashboard in frustration. The next day, though, you may greet the same problem with a shrug of the shoulders and accept that the traffic jam is nothing more than a trivial nuisance. The stressor is the same, but for one reason or another, you and your brain have shifted from anger to acceptance in a matter of hours, so the reaction is vastly different. It is this unpredictability that makes stress so complex.

Maybe we need to spend more time focusing on our reaction to stress than the things that trigger it.

The physiology of stress

Whether danger is tangible, eg being confronted by a snake, or generated in your own psyche, eg the fears you may feel when walking down a dark alley late at night, the physiological response to stress will be consistent. Initially, there will be a rapid release of adrenaline and noradrenaline. The former dilates the bronchial tubes in your lungs, accelerating the heart rate and elevating blood pressure, meaning that a greater amount of oxygen can both enter and be pumped around the body. Noradrenaline inhibits the activity of the parasympathetic nervous system, resulting in the pupils of the eyes becoming dilated, something that will enhance vision, while the volume of blood flowing to the gut will be reduced (this is not a time when digestion is a top priority) and diverted to muscles, preparing them for action. Thanks to the speedy release of adrenaline and noradrenaline, you have an instantaneous ability to respond. This is often referred to as the 'fight or flight' response.

Of equal note is the fact that these chemicals have a half-life of two to three minutes, meaning that shortly after the stressor is removed, the physiological changes you have undergone are likely to reverse and you will calm down.

Stress in excess

If stress can be good for you, why does it seem to be at the root of so many problems? The answer is that there is a tipping point where the loads that are placed on your body and brain outweigh the coping mechanisms that you have at your disposal. Put simply, the systems in your body become fatigued and your physical and mental capabilities diminish. If this is persistent, poor health is a possibility.

If you are placed under a significant one-off load of stress, such as a bereavement or being made redundant, you may hurtle towards the tipping point. At other times, the tipping point can creep up on you as a multitude of low-level stressors mount up, gradually increasing the strain on your system until the final straw is placed upon the camel's back. Then boom! You break.

In some ways this is similar to a physics experiment that you may have performed at school where you gradually increase the weight placed on a spring and observe what happens to it. Low-level loads make no difference and the spring does not budge, but as the weight increases, the spring starts to stretch. Eventually the demand becomes too much and the spring breaks.

You may also remember being asked to draw a graph looking at the relationship between the load and the length of spring; you are less likely to remember that this graph is called a stress-strain curve. This could even have been one of your first interactions with stress. The other thing you may have been asked to note was the moment the load permanently affected the recoil property of the spring, in other words the point at which the spring didn't fully return to its resting state if the load was removed. This is the point where the spring was no longer fully effective, something that is called plastic deformity.

In many ways, human beings are similar to the spring. Initially, we can function perfectly well under a certain amount of load, but if the demands exceed our resilience capacity, permanent scars can appear. And if the stress becomes excessive, we can break in either our performance or our health, or both.

The analogy of the spring is simple and easy to relate to, but as humans are a bit more complicated than springs, I need to add a couple of caveats. First, the variations in people's genetics, experiences and environments are considerable. While the structure of a spring is constant, we need to consider an inordinate number of variables when comparing person to person. Second, the experiment features one type of load that pulls on the system in a uniform direction. If only life was as simple as this! Loads can come at us from many directions and in many guises – from the emotional to the intellectual, the physical and the environmental, we can be challenged in so many ways. And this is a further reason why stress is hard to simplify.

Excessive stress and the body

If you put an excessive physical load through a tendon, ligament or bone, it can break; but this type of sudden overload is not the sort of stress that I mean by stress-related illnesses. In these cases, the stress does not directly damage a tissue; instead, it tends to either activate or inhibit hormones in our body.

Hormones are chemicals secreted by glands, typically carried in the blood stream, that help control many bodily functions. For example, insulin regulates the level of sugar in our blood and aldosterone regulates the level of electrolytes. I have already mentioned the effect of adrenaline and the neurotransmitter nor-adrenaline and how these are essential in times of emergency, but if we are in need of support for long periods of time, these hormonal caped crusaders fade away and are replaced by cortisol.

Cortisol has a bad reputation. Despite having a role to play in metabolising blood sugar and controlling blood pressure, it can have a corrosive effect on the body. One of the main challenges presented by cortisol is that, with a chemical half-life of more than an hour, it loiters in our system, and if levels rise significantly, the risk of stroke and kidney disease increase and the competency of the cardiovascular system is threatened. So far, I have highlighted the hormones that become more prevalent in times of stress, but there are others that are inhibited. One reduction of note is in the level of the prostaglandins, chemicals that have a key role in neutralising the damaging impact gastric acid can have on the lining of the stomach. If this dampening effect is reduced, the stomach becomes more prone to ulceration, and if the gastric acid escapes upwards into the oesophagus, we can experience the symptom of heartburn. Many feel this symptom is innocuous, but it's something that can increase the risk of oesoph-ageal cancer. Heartburn to cancer is a significant jump, but by addressing what may seem to be trivial, maybe you won't have to deal with the serious.

Excessive stress and the brain

As well as an impact on the body, stress has the potential to scar the brain. An elevation in cortisol levels can increase the amount of myelin, a substance that creates a sheath around cells known as neurons, and this results in the inefficient transfer of information along the nerve highways. Our speed and clarity of thinking can be compromised.

But this is not the only negative impact. Excessive cortisol can:

- Reduce the amount of brain-derived neurotrophic factor, a substance that aids the health of brain cells

- Reduce the amount of grey matter in the prefrontal cortex, the part of the brain that delivers what are known as executive functions – paying attention, planning, decision making and regulating emotions

- Impair the hippocampus, an area that is important for spatial memory

- Activate the amygdala, an area often considered to be the fear centre of the brain

A final consideration is the negative impact that stress can have on self-esteem and confidence. Our ego, psyche and mood can deteriorate – life can feel incredibly tough.

Measuring stress

Measuring the impact of a load placed on a spring is relatively easy; evaluating stress at a human level is a much trickier thing to do. Broadly speaking, there are two possibilities: subjective opinion or objective data.

Subjective checks

Asking someone to score themselves out of ten as to how energised, happy, relaxed or positive they are feeling can be of benefit. If we do this consistently, we can derive benefit by looking at the trend of the scores we award ourselves, but with the responses depending purely on the subjective, fault lines can develop with this approach as our answers can be influenced by a multitude of variables. Why am I being asked that? How should I reply? The article in this morning's newspaper was highlighting how everyone is stressed at the moment – does that mean I am too?

Having worked with sporting organisations and seen how questionnaires can be used, I have witnessed how people may think about an outcome before delivering their honest answer. A youngster who is on the verge of making their debut for the first team is unlikely to say they are feeling stressed and fatigued in the weekly wellbeing survey – if they do, there is a reduced chance of selection. Equally, the old pro who ticks the box saying they are feeling somewhat fatigued knows full well their training load is likely to be reduced and that their week will suddenly become much easier. The questionnaire approach is easy to manipulate.

More complex tools can be beneficial in the clinical setting, but they are often wordy and unlikely to work for someone who wants a quick check-in with themselves to see how they are feeling.

When working with someone who is struggling to identify what is really stressing them I will ask them to complete a simple audit, an example is shown below. The important thing is to evaluate not just the problem, but also to consider the 'emotional tariff' – how the problem really matters to you. By offering a score between one and three that looks at the challenge, and multiplying it by another number, again scored between one and three, that looks at the tariff, the more significant stressors can be identified and the exercise sometimes unearths the less obvious.

List what has stressed you over the past week

Problem	Pain in the butt tariff	Emotional tariff	Score
Snapped at a colleague	2	2	4
Staffing levels	2	1	2
Parent fallen	3	3	9
Argument with partner	2	3	6
Christmas rota	1	2	2
Totals	10	11	110

Optima table of a stress audit

In summary, questionnaires provide an overview, but they are merely a spot check of a perception, sometimes the view can be clouded.

Objective checks

If stress creates a physiological response, then looking at a physiological parameter makes sense, and there are a number of possibilities. Many consider that the measurement of salivary cortisol is the gold standard, but due to the need for laboratory analysis, the result is likely to be received days after the test. So while this may offer an accurate evaluation, the practicalities mean that the moment may well have passed.

If you are looking for a measurement that provides an immediate insight, the heart provides two possibilities:

- **Resting heart rate.** Measured in beats per minute, heart rate is used across the fitness world to determine the level of cardiovascular demands of exercise. In addition to providing a view on the effort of training, resting heart rate can be used to evaluate how the body has recovered. In simple terms, a low resting heart rate is likely to mean you are recovering well and coping with the demands of life.

- **Heart rate variability (HRV)** is another metric that is derived from the heart. Instead of looking at the

total beats per minute, HRV looks at the pattern
of the beats. This is known as the beat to beat
or R to R interval and provides a view on the
functionality of the autonomic nervous system.

The autonomic nervous system controls all the things
we don't think about, such as breathing, digestion,
sweating, heart rate and blood pressure, and it consists
of two branches. The sympathetic branch becomes
more active when our bodies are stressed, while the
parasympathetic branch is more active when the body
is looking to recharge and recover.

If understanding sympathetic and parasympathetic
activity provides insight into how stressed someone is, the challenge is in evaluating how this part
of the nervous system is functioning, and this is
where HRV has its use. When sympathetic tone is
dominant, the heart will beat in a highly metronomic
pattern – a heart rate of sixty beats a minute would
show a regular pattern of one beat every second.
When parasympathetic tone is dominant, the heart
has a tendency to follow a cycle of beating quickly
for three or four seconds, and then slowing for a similar time. The total beats per minute can still be sixty,
but there is a markedly different pattern.

There are pluses and minuses with both heart rate and
HRV. While heart rate is easier to understand, HRV
can potentially provide greater insight. Over the past
decade, I have used HRV to help people understand

how they are coping with life. I am biased towards it, and with over 10,000 days and nights' worth of data available, I am keen to use it in this book to illustrate some of the factors that will potentially allow or inhibit you when it comes to scoring the goals required to win this game of life.

For reference, here is an example of a twenty-four-hour chart with explanations of what the various shades mean. This will be useful when you're looking at some of the case studies featured in the subsequent chapters.

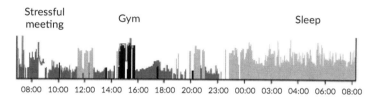

Graph showing a day's activities

- Mid-grey shading – this indicates when the body is in a state of sympathetic dominance that occurs when it is loaded/stressed. This is typically seen during the day.

- Dark shading – this indicates physical activity. In this example, the person had been doing interval training.

- Light grey shading – this indicates when the body is in a state of parasympathetic dominance that occurs when it is recovering and recharging. It is typically seen during sleep.

NB: the height of the bars is not associated with a unit of measurement, but does indicate the dominance of either the load or recovery reaction. High level of mid-grey shading can be considered high stress whereas high light grey bars can be considered high recovery.

That brings the theory section of the book to a close. It's now time for you to think a bit more closely about you!

SECTION 2

THE FIRST GOAL: YOU AND YOUR WELLBEING

The advice that exists on nutrition, exercise, sleep and relationships is widespread, the evidence to back it up considerable and the access to support, whether it be digital or face to face, abundant. Why is it then that the foundation stones that underpin our health, wellbeing and performance are ignored by so many? Why does the obvious become the obsolete?

There are likely to be many answers, but one factor that commonly arises is that people rarely think about why they should look after themselves. They may consider it at a superficial level, but have not identified the purpose, or underlying importance, they require to create a strong attachment to a habit.

This section has three aims. It starts by helping you to identify your purpose, then provides some information on the basic ingredients you need for your health and wellbeing, and ends with a template that will help you formulate a plan that works for you. Do this and you can say you have scored the first goal; ignore it, and your chances of successfully scoring the second and third are likely to be slim.

3
Understanding Yourself

M any years ago, I used HRV with a nurse who specialised in cancer care. She was feeling tired and low on energy, and she wanted to understand how she was dealing with the demands of work, and how effectively she was recovering in her life away from it.

On one of the days, when wearing the monitor, she had to deliver a clinic where incredibly sick patients (and their families) would be updated on treatment, progress and their prognosis. This was a tough day at the office; one that we both thought would be high on stress.

The graph below shows the physiological state of her autonomic nervous system on the day of the clinic:

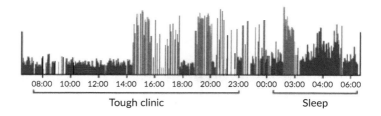

Optima graph showing physiological states

The data clearly shows that the clinic, which took place in the afternoon, was not draining the nurse at all – in fact, it could be said the opposite was true and it was energising her. But it also shows poor quality sleep. This opened my eyes to the importance of looking at things with an open mind.

Both the nurse and I were surprised to see her body's physiological response while she was delivering tough messages to patients. But the more I monitor people the more I have understood that when doing something that is closely aligned to personal values and competencies, in an environment where you are happy, trusting and comfortable with colleagues, it is possible to see a restorative physiological effect.

The second gem I took away from this reading came from a discussion we had about sleep. It went something like this:

Nurse: 'My sleep is not very good, is it?'

Me: 'I have certainly seen better.'

Nurse: 'Why do you think that is?'

Me: 'It could be that the challenges from the clinic are having an impact. Maybe there is a latent affect, and you are struggling to detach from work.'

Nurse (after some thought): 'I am not sure that is the case. I love my work. I have done that clinic for many years and feel that I am good at separating myself from it.'

Me: 'What did you do in the evening when you got home?'

Nurse: 'I would have been doing some reading and a bit of writing.'

Me: 'Tell me more about that.'

Nurse: 'I've got to get my PhD submitted in a few weeks' time, so I am frantically working on that. Oh, and I was travelling to China the next day, so I was sorting things out for this trip, too.'

This conversation taught me a couple of invaluable lessons. First, don't jump to the obvious conclusion. Both of us had thought the clinic would have been the toughest part of the day, but from a physiological point of view, it was not. Having seen thousands of days' worth of data, I should have realised that it is so often the submaximal stressors – the ones that nag away underneath the surface – that create significant challenges to good-quality sleep. The big stuff can sometimes be easier to deal with as you are likely to see it, process it and move on from it; it is the smaller challenges that can slip through your conscience and end up being the catalyst for fatigue.

Evaluating life with depth and breadth is important if you want to seek out the annoyances as well as the catastrophes. How often do you ask yourself these three questions?

- How am I looking after myself physically and mentally?

- How am I looking after what is important to me?

- What are the challenges that are getting under my skin at the moment?

The second lesson I learned during my work with the nurse related to the physiological response when someone is doing something that is aligned with their personal values and mission, or doing something they love.

Many companies have a mission statement to describe their intent and modus operandi, but how many individuals can truly articulate what is important to them? Coming up with your mission statement will require some thought and talking; it is likely to take time but it is a valuable exercise to do.

To give you an example, here is my current mission statement:

> I want to be respected as a physiotherapist and a thought leader in my field. I want to run a company where no job is too big for the organisation and no person is too big for the job. And my immediate family is the most important thing in my life.

It is simple, but I chose the themes and words carefully. If I have one of those awkward dilemmas that life occasionally throws at us, I find that a check-in with the statement is likely to lead me to the best option.

Ultimately, a mission statement is a way of reminding yourself what really makes you tick. If you are living a life that is closely aligned to the statement, you will give yourself a better chance to be resilient, healthy, comfortable in your own skin and doing your job well. If you are living a life where your actions are a million miles from your values, you may well be an accident waiting to happen.

Sleep

Sleep, something we do for around 30% of our lives, is likely to be one of our most deliberate coping mechanisms, and yet it is something many people pay extraordinarily little attention to. While many have ignored it, researchers have not and with a tripling in peer-reviewed journal articles seen between 2005 and 2015, our understanding of sleep has increased dramatically. From controlling blood sugar to shooting a basketball accurately, and performing intellectual tasks to controlling emotions, researchers have unearthed a multitude of benefits.

The function of sleep is not simply to give the body and mind a rest; it is to restore, re-energise and refresh. The phrase 'sleep is for wimps', so popular in the 1980s, has not stood the test of time as it has become clear that sleep is good for our health, wellbeing and performance.

What does good-quality sleep look like? Well, an adult human being needs to go through five complete cycles to achieve restorative sleep. Experts are likely to break each cycle down into a multitude of phases and subphases, but for the sake of simplicity, let's look at the main divisions.

- Phase 1 – transitional sleep. This occurs when we first go to sleep and, to a lesser extent, between the end of rapid eye movement/REM sleep and the start of the next theta phase. Our heartbeat, rate of breathing and eye movements will drop and our muscles will relax.

- Phase 2 – theta sleep. At this point, our body temperature drops, eye movements will be minimal and the brain disconnects with the travails of the past twenty-four hours.

- Phase 3 – delta sleep. Here, there is an increase in the release of growth hormones, and the emphasis is on physical repair and restoration.

- Phase 4 – rapid eye movement (REM) sleep. This is considered to be the time when dreams are most prominent. The level of cortisol reduces, brain cells are re-energised and learning is embedded.

NB: for those who sleep deeply through the night, it is likely that the time they spend in transitional sleep will be minimal or non-existent after the first cycle.

The average duration of a sleep cycle is around ninety minutes, meaning that, for most, eight hours' sleep should do the trick. There will always be outliers with some people only requiring six hours, while others may need nine hours plus. This variation is due to the average length of delta sleep, which can differ considerably at an individual level. For some, this will be forty minutes; for others, it will be ninety minutes; for most, it will be close to sixty minutes.

You may have noted that I used the word 'average' when referring to the duration of delta sleep. This is because the minutes per delta cycle tend to diminish as the night goes on – in other words, physical restoration takes place in the front end of sleep. On the other hand, REM sleep behaves in the opposite way, becoming more prominent in the latter part of sleep. There are many further subtle variations in the architecture of sleep, but one simple message holds true – if you want both body and brain to recover and recharge, you need to get good-quality sleep throughout the night.

The best way to measure the effectiveness of sleep is to study brainwaves using an electroencephalogram, a complex procedure where ten to twenty electrodes are attached at defined points on the scalp. In terms of self-monitoring, this technique is impractical, however, with advances in wearable technology, evaluating sleep in the home setting, albeit in a rudimentary way, has now become possible. Either through the measurement of movement (actigraphy) or the pattern of the heartbeat (HRV), this monitoring provides an overview of the quality of sleep and supplies people with some basic insight.

If you are struggling with your sleep or want to know why you are not sleeping so well, there are several factors that can make the difference between restoration and insomnia.

Fixtures and fittings

In the world of elite sport, the attention to minute detail is significant. Often referred to as the one-percenters, they are the details that can make the difference between triumph and failure, so the search for marginal gains is relentless. Adjustments to training, equipment, clothing or travel are commonplace, and so is the approach to optimising the sleep of an athlete.

If an athlete is travelling for a month-long training camp, it is quite possible that their own sleeping accessories, from pillow to mattress, will travel with them. While it is totally impractical for a business traveller to lug their mattress around the world, there are some who will take a pillow. Even if that is not possible, many hotels offer a range so being proactive and choosing a pillow that is likely to work best for you, something that takes a matter of minutes, can produce a considerable upside.

Many people have experienced a hotel room where the temperature is too hot, so much so they toss and turn, open windows and throw the duvet from one side of the bed to the other. The Sleep Council advises that an ideal temperature for an adult human being to sleep at is 16–18° centigrade, with the caveat that elderly people may find a slightly warmer room beneficial. If you can influence the temperature of your sleeping environment, do it before you go to bed rather than reacting in the midst of a sleep-disturbed night. Isn't it better to address the environment before going to sleep rather than the middle of the night?

Light

Daylight helps with the release of melatonin, a hormone that has a role to play in regulating our circadian rhythm, but not all light is good for us. The biggest culprit is blue light, part of the spectrum that is commonly emitted by the screens of mobile phones and computers, and even with a blue-light filter, it is likely that some will seep through. The effect is that the pineal gland will be stimulated and dopamine, a hormone that makes us feel alert, is released – not ideal just before bed.

Here are some useful tips that may help:

- If you have to use a screen in the evening, consider buying some blue-light filter glasses.

- If you have a television in your bedroom, consider moving it. As a minimum, ensure it is switched off at the wall – the standby light can be a real irritant.

- Invest in an eye mask, the type often provided on aeroplanes. Not only are they a great way to create the darkness you require to sleep soundly, but the simple act of putting the eye mask on can act as a psychological cue, prompting the brain to recognise it is now time for sleep.

- If you have to engage with electronic devices late in the evening, consider the content. Watching a thriller or checking the news is not always the best 'bedtime story'!

Noise

This is likely to disrupt most people's sleep. Whether it is a party in the upstairs flat, the traffic in your street or the airways of your partner causing the disturbance, it is something that should be addressed.

A simple solution to the party problem could be to purchase some high-quality earplugs. These may also help deal with the bed partner who snores, although it is a mystery to me why so many people don't get to grips with a medical condition that can impact health and relationships.

Sleep apnoea means the tongue falls backwards onto the soft palate of the upper mouth, partially blocking the entry of air into the lungs and resulting in a cacophony of disruptive noise as the air tries to force its way past the obstruction. In serious cases, the tongue creates such a barrier that air entry is impaired totally. The brain senses this and rouses the sufferer who will shift position and clear their airway.

The problem is that the sleeper soon shifts back to the original position, the obstruction re-emerges and the corrective reflex will have to kick in again. This constant cycle of disturbance means the quality of sleep can be seriously compromised.

The common side-effect of excessive tiredness is an inclination to fall asleep during the day. This may seem trivial, but with an increased risk of type 2 diabetes, cardiovascular disease and stroke also associated with sleep apnoea, the condition needs to be taken seriously.

Of course it is not only those with sleep apnoea who suffer. Excessive snoring can be tiring for their partners, too. It is in everyone's interest for the condition to be treated, so I would urge you to seek medical advice if your snoring is influencing either you or your partner's energy level. The positive effect of treatment can be dramatic, and the improvement in mood and general health – of both parties – highly significant.

Food and drink

Food can be either friend or foe when it comes to its relationship with good-quality sleep, depending on what you eat and drink, and when you eat or drink it. With so many different approaches to nutrition, I will leave the 'friend' part to the books that specialise in this area, but it is worth saying that if you try to sleep soon after eating, in particular a meal that is high in sugar or other forms of simple carbohydrate, your sleep quality is likely to lower.

Conversely, going to bed on an empty stomach is not ideal. A baby, when hungry, wakes and cries. While an adult may not resort to tears, it is likely that the quality of their sleep will be compromised.

Alcohol

Mood, speech and the ability to stand up can be a challenge if too much alcohol is taken on board, but one effect that is not so obvious is the negative impact it can have on sleep. The example below shows data for the same person on two consecutive nights:

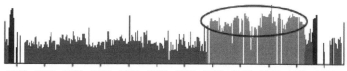

10:00 12:00 14:00 16:00 18:00 20:00 23:00 00:00 03:00 04:00 06:00 08:00

Night 1 Bed at 11.30
No alcohol
90% of sleep time is effective

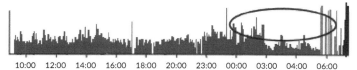

10:00 12:00 14:00 16:00 18:00 20:00 23:00 00:00 03:00 04:00 06:00

Night 2 Bed at 11.30
5 units of alcohol
14% of sleep time is effective

Optima graph comparison of two consecutive nights

Typically, for every unit of alcohol that is drunk in an evening, people lose an hour's worth of quality sleep. While there will always be outliers, alcohol has a dramatic effect on many individuals' quality of sleep.

Bearing this in mind, I'm amazed at how many people come through the door after a tough day at work and resort to a couple of glasses of wine or a stiff gin and tonic, and rely on alcohol as a habitual coping mechanism. They may feel better momentarily, it may send them to sleep, but if their recovery is impacted to the extent the graph shows, the next day is likely to find them feeling lethargic, struggling to think with clarity and communicating ineffectively.

Stimulants

The effect of caffeine on sleep is well-known, but nicotine is another stimulant that can affect the quality of our sleep. Triggering the release of adrenaline and dopamine, it has the potential to both relax and excite us. The former may be good for sleep, but feeling alert with elevated adrenaline levels is not.

With a half-life of around two hours, nicotine doesn't linger in our system for as long as caffeine, but it is still worth reducing our intake in the latter part of the day. And, of course, if nicotine is delivered through a traditional cigarette, other health challenges, especially relating to the cardiovascular and respiratory systems, may hinder good-quality sleep.

Switching off the mind

Many people are good at putting their bodies to rest. Their head hits the pillow and they are asleep in an instant. Not so many people are good at switching their minds off, and while they sleep, their grey matter can be working overtime. These are the people who habitually wake at three or four in the morning and struggle to get back to sleep, the people who need to create a formal way to switch off their mind before they sleep. Learning how to fully detach from the demands of the day and calm the mind down is a trait that I often see in people who are both successful and balanced.

While some rely on reading or watching television, and others may meditate or perform some breathing exercises, I have to class these activities as distraction therapies. They take the mind away from current content and temporarily turn it towards something new and, while providing a short-term benefit, do they really fully switch the mind off? The trouble is that once the book is closed or the meditation finished, the mind can pick up from where it left off.

A simple technique to help here is using the today-tomorrow list. If you are going through a really busy time in life, whether it be work or social, around forty-five minutes before bed, find a blank page in a notebook, draw a line down the middle of the page and create two columns. In the left-hand column, make notes on what you have done today. This is designed to make you feel better about life – it certainly works for me. In the right-hand column, write down what you have to do tomorrow. Once you've done this, look at the list, take a few deep breaths and create a feeling of control. Then close the book and accept that it and its contents can be put to bed for the night. The list is not going anywhere and you have given your brain permission to switch off.

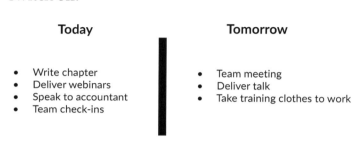

Today	Tomorrow
• Write chapter • Deliver webinars • Speak to accountant • Team check-ins	• Team meeting • Deliver talk • Take training clothes to work

An example of a today/tomorrow list

In summary, sleep is an important and often neglected pillar of health. It is also essential for our performance. In investigations relating to disasters, such as the devastating explosion that was suffered by the Space Shuttle Challenger to the accident at Chernobyl, fatigue is cited as a contributory factor. These events are extreme, but with The Royal Society for the Prevention of Accidents suggesting that approximately 20% of road-traffic incidents are related to driver fatigue, maybe the dramatic consequences of poor sleep are slightly closer to home than we'd like to think. Many companies now have a fatigue-management policy – what does your personal plan look like?

Exercise

The positive correlation between physical activity and improvements to blood pressure, sleep, mental health, blood sugar levels and even creativity is undisputed. This is hardly breaking news, but despite this, some consider exercise a chore, others just don't do it and a number of people actively rebel against it.

Before we go any further, let me assure you that health-promoting physical activity does not necessarily mean sport, nor does it involve the ownership of Lycra-rich clothing or state-of-the-art trainers; not even membership of the local gym is compulsory. It doesn't necessarily require you to walk a certain number of steps or do thirty minutes of exercise five times a week; it does mean working at an intensity and for a duration that creates the desired cardio-respiratory response – 10,000 dawdles or ambles simply does not do the job.

From a health point of view, it means engaging in an activity that creates some demand on the cardio-respiratory system. If you find when you're walking, dancing or gardening that the rate and depth of your breathing has increased to a level where, if you tried to talk, you have to catch your breath mid-sentence, it is likely the activity you are undertaking is sufficient to promote health.

I'm not going to provide you with a detailed training programme – if you want one of those, seek the appropriate professional advice. Instead, I wish to provide some food for thought. Just a couple of 'snacks', one that will be relevant to those who do exercise, but firstly one for those who don't.

A sedentary lifestyle can be cited as a barrier to exercise, but I suspect a bigger challenge comes from people's minds. If you are struggling to engage with exercise or simply can't be bothered, it can be useful to create an emotional attachment. Instead of thinking about activity as a chore, connect it to something that is important to you.

The examples are numerous:

- Keeping up with the rest of the family when out for a bike ride.

- Being able to help your 85-year-old father up the stairs.

- Not being like your elderly father when you walk up the stairs when you reach the age of 85.

- The legitimacy you will feel as a leader when you talk to your colleagues about the importance of looking after yourself and the importance of energy.

- Better mental health and feeling happy.

All these are examples of emotional anchors that can prove to be the catalyst that hook you into the habit of healthy exercise.

The second 'snack for thought' is for those who exercise with the intention of becoming fitter yet pay little attention to how they are using their time. They are committed to exercise and week in, week out repeat the same run, typically at the same time, or check in to the gym every other day and follow the same programme fifty-two weeks a year. This approach is fine if your aim is to be healthy, switch the mind off and detach from other aspects of life, but it is not great if you want to improve speed, strength or stamina.

Rather than creating a variation in load that will lead to an adaptive response, these regular exercisers have created what I refer to as 'habitual drift'. If improving your fitness is the goal, then the attachment you require is not so much with the emotions, but with the knowledge that a good personal trainer will have.

CASE STUDY – WHAT IS GOOD EXERCISE?

Clients often ask whether an exercise session is good or bad. Unless they know what they are trying to achieve, it is impossible to judge.

The graphs below show data relating to two pieces of exercise, done by the same person, both lasting an hour. The darkened area shows the heart rate, the lighter line indicates something called excess post-exercise oxygen

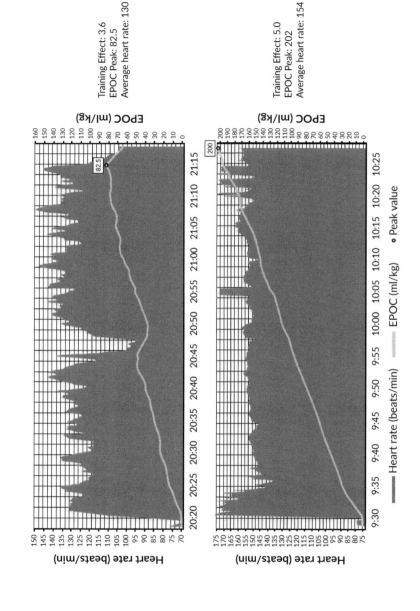

consumption (EPOC) that is measured in ml of oxygen per kg of body weight. From this, we can derive a training effect, a score between 1 and 5 that provides a view on the cardio-respiratory intensity of the training.

In the first chart, a training effect of 3.6 is seen as the exercise produced a cardio-respiratory response that is considered 'improving'. The second chart shows a training effect of 5.0 – a level that is known as 'overreaching' and one that produces a very high level of demand on the cardio-respiratory system.
Which one of these is the better exercise? If the aim is to go flat out, then it's the second session; if the goal is for more manageable load, then the output seen in the first session is more appropriate.

If you are looking to judge whether your training session is good or bad (and with watches and devices available that provide a running commentary while you are exercising, ignorance is not an acceptable excuse), you need to think about what you want to achieve before you do it. Blood, sweat and tears is not always the correct formula.

Nutrition

What have you eaten and drunk in the last twenty-four hours? Write it down, and I mean everything, so please include snacks, sweets and other edible accessories.

Once you have done that, pass a critical eye over the list and give yourself a score out of ten for 'nutritional magnificence', ten being top of the class and zero being the depths of dietary despair. If you have achieved ten out of ten – bravo! But this is rare, and for most people, there is usually plenty of room for improvement.

It is not until you write things down and see them in black and white that you realise just how you have been fuelling your brain and body, so my first suggestion on this topic is that you become more mindful about what you eat as food can either be your friend or your foe.

In addition to examining what you are eating, ask the questions when and why. It may be you eat a certain item at a certain time of day due to a habit that has been embedded for years. It could be a foundation stone of social interaction or the need for comfort, possibly even an addiction. Of course, at the most basic level we eat to survive, but I am going to suggest that you become a tad more ambitious than mere survival. Adopt the attitude that you eat to perform.

EXAMPLE – FUELLING FOR A LONG DAY

Let me give you a simple example. A few years ago, I was engaged by an organisation based in Scotland to deliver a series of workshops. These days would involve an early start, and typically I would be sitting in the departure lounge of Luton Airport by 6am. On arrival, I would deliver two sessions, and then catch the flight back from Edinburgh at around 20.30.

These days were draining, both physically and mentally. With a variety of airport outlets available for breakfast, I would shun my preferred pain au chocolate and ensure that I had porridge and some fruit. Then I would buy a sandwich and more fruit so that I had something to keep me going between sessions.

Did I do this for my health? Was it influenced by my waistline or cholesterol level? To be honest, the answer is no. The reason I made the healthier choice was because I wanted to do my job well. I did something positive to counter what I knew would be a challenging day. If we take this a step further, I was doing something to help ensure the organisation asked me back. Shallow maybe, but I needed food to be my friend on these long days.

If you find that food is a chore or you struggle to make the right choices, it may be useful to focus not on the negative consequences of eating badly, but outputs such as energy and health. All of a sudden, a better diet becomes a highly attractive option.

With so many dietary messages in the public domain it can be tough to know where to start, especially with the increasing awareness towards intolerances and allergies. In the same way I advise the exerciser to tap into the knowledge of fitness experts, I will reinforce that it can be highly valuable to invest in some bespoke nutritional advice.

While some may pay considerable attention to the solids they eat, an area of diet that is often ignored is the fluids that are drunk. Water is critical, with research identifying several negative consequences if dehydrated: a 2% deficit results in the reduction of physical and mental capability by between 4–8%. If the deficit increases to 4%, productivity can deteriorate by between 20–30%. At 5%, physical symptoms such as headaches become prevalent, and at 10% plus, dehydration can become a serious health condition. There is much advice on how much water people should drink a day, with 2 litres being a commonly quoted figure, but I suggest you consider a different approach. On a hot day, it is likely you will need to drink more than on a cold one, so rather than relying on a number that offers generic guidance, focus on how you are feeling. Become adaptive to your own needs rather than following a prescription for the masses and, whatever the weather, try to avoid a feeling of thirstiness.

From coffee, tea and cola to energy drinks and chocolate, caffeine is found in many things we may drink and eat on a daily basis. A stimulant of the central nervous system, caffeine appears to have both health and performance benefits, and there is evidence to suggest a link to reducing the risk of liver disease and cardiovascular pathology. In the sporting world, caffeine appeared on the World Anti-Doping Agency list of banned substances up until 2004; it is now permitted and used by many athletes as an ergogenic (energy enhancing) aid. Caffeine is not all bad.

However, for all its benefits, caffeine can present some challenges, especially when we take it on board either late in the day or in significant amounts. It is a stimulant that acts on the brain by occupying receptors designed for adenosine, a compound that is particularly useful in regulating sleep. If these receptors are blocked, adenosine is unable to act and prepare our system for an effective night's sleep.

The chemical half-life of caffeine is around five hours. The relevance here is that if you take on board a significant amount of caffeine late in the day, this stimulant could still be in your system at a time when you are thinking about going to bed.

For example, if you decide to pop into a coffee shop on your commute home at 5pm and order a large filter coffee, you could be putting around 250mg caffeine into your system. Five hours later, at around 10pm, you would still have 125mg of the stimulant creating havoc. It is worth considering the timing and dosage of your caffeine intake with care.

Contrary to many people's perception, alcohol is not a stimulant; it actually acts as an inhibitor or depressant. The confusion may arise as one of the first actions of alcohol is to suppress part of the brain that controls emotions. Put this alongside the increased release of serotonin, a hormone that makes us feel happy, and we can understand why mirth and merriment are associated with small amounts of alcohol. But if we take more alcohol on board, other areas of the brain, such as the controllers of speech and co-ordination, are inhibited, increasing the possibility that words can become slurred and walking in a straight line a tricky test of co-ordination; and, as already covered, alcohol does not provide people with restorative sleep.

Nutrition can undoubtedly be your friend or foe. When times are tough, consider how food and drink can help you rather than adopting a poorer diet, which may well simply add to the challenges you are facing.

Now that we have had a look at some of the basic ingredients that can enable you to stay energised and, indeed, healthy it's time to think about how you can be more successful in implementing your plan to look after *you*, and score that all-important first goal.

4
Creating Your Plan

I am sure you know someone who has made a New Year's resolution – it may even have been you. However, are you in the group of 77% who give up in week one or are you an exemplar of resolve and aligned with the 19% who are still on track at two years?

Why is it that going to the gym twice a week, reading one book a month or leaving work on time seems so appealing and easy to do on 1 January, and yet for many, it's nigh on impossible a few days later? Why do people find it so hard to deliver the dream? In some instances, the goal may have been totally unrealistic and defeat an inevitability, but in others, the inertia is often due to a lack of focus, an absence of accountability and minimal emotional attachment.

Having a method around goal setting and reviewing can help.

Goals: From SMART to SMARTIES

First proffered by George T Doran, the specific, measurable, adaptable, realistic and time-bound (SMART) methodology has been adapted in several ways over the years. For example, realistic is sometimes replaced with relevant, and more recently the acronym has been extended to SMARTER with the additional letters promoting the themes of evaluation and re-adjustment.

Building on this, you may find it useful to use the SMARTIES acronym. This incorporates a couple of additional steps into the process and provides a structure for setting, evaluating and achieving personal goals.

EXAMPLE – THE SMARTIES WAY TO BE HEALTHY

The dream – I want to be healthy.

Specific – What does being healthy mean to you? Is it losing weight? Exercising more? Reducing sickness absence from work? Without clarity of what healthy really means, any progress you make will be through chance rather than judgement.

Measurable – If the goal is losing weight, how much? Exercise how often? Reduce sickness absence to what?

Adaptable – Sometimes advances will be better or achieved more quickly than you expected, while there may be other times when progress is tortuous and tough. Whatever the pace, there is no harm in adjusting the goalposts and resetting the vision, especially if the other option is to give up.

For example, if you have suffered an injury, how will you adapt your goal of exercising more?

Realistic – Being healthy is a realistic goal for most. Playing centre forward for Barcelona is within the capabilities of only a few, and nigh on impossible if you are 43 years old. The goal must be in line with reality.

Time-bound – Clarity around when you will achieve the goal avoids drift and creates motivation. For example, when do you intend to lose the weight by?

Inspected – When and how are you going to pause to see how you are progressing? Who can provide help in keeping you accountable? For example, will you weigh yourself every two weeks, reveal the result to a friend and set a new fortnightly goal?

Ego – How much has the goal come from within, as opposed to being forced upon you? Give yourself a score out of ten that indicates how important the outcome is to you. If the score is below eight, then failure or disengagement is likely to be on the horizon.

Separation – This asks a similar question, but instead of thinking how important success is to you, ask how important it is to others. Ideally, both scores should be high; if there is a gap between the two, then you may need to do some work on alignment before taking the first step.

Emotional attachment

The SMARTIES structure highlights the phrase 'emotional attachment'. Before unleashing yourself on a path of action, you really need to think it through and create understanding around its importance to you. To do this, ask yourself the question: why am I really bothering with this?

Better still is to ask someone who knows you well to ask you the question, and get them to push your thinking so that you can clearly articulate the reason.

EXAMPLE – WHY DO YOU WANT TO BE HEALTHY?

'I want to be healthy.'

'Who doesn't – why do you want to be healthy?'

'It seems like a sensible thing to do.'

'Yep – I get that, but why do you want to be healthy?'

'Well, I've not been feeling quite myself recently.'

'Really – tell me more about that.'

'I've just been down on energy. I have felt tired and started to snap at my partner.'

'Anything else?'

'I was really frustrated with myself at the weekend. I had promised to take the kids to the park on Sunday afternoon, but fell asleep on the sofa.'

'What did they say?'

'They didn't say anything. When I woke up, they just had this look of disappointment in their eyes. I felt dreadful.'

I'm sure you can see where the conversation is going. This person may want to be healthy, but the emotional attachment is elsewhere. The goal they really desire is a better relationship with their children. If they frame the goal around the latter, it is likely they will have a better chance of sticking to their exercise plan.

Ask for help

Achieving anything in life on your own can be an uphill battle. Not only can other people offer direct assistance, they can provide support and hold you to account.

I told several people that I was writing a book because I knew that when I spoke to them again, they would be likely to ask me how the writing was going. Not only did this keep me on track, but most people I told responded with encouragement, offering to be a sounding board for ideas, proofreading, etc. In general, people like helping others, but not many are mind readers. They can maybe make an educated guess, but they won't know your specific goals and the help you'll need to achieve them unless you ask, so don't be shy. In this day and age, asking for help is not a sign of weakness, but should be considered to be a sign of strength.

Accountability

For all the internal desire you may have to achieve a goal, for all the help and advice that others give, you may still find that success is elusive unless you put in place a formal system of accountability. A good example would be joining one of the many organisations that help people lose weight. They provide dietary advice, psychological support, forums and friendship, but for many, the most important part of the programme will be the weekly weigh-in. This is where the attendee is confronted with their success or failure – for many, it's the stimulus that makes the biggest difference.

Creating an accountability system that works for you requires some thought. If you think back to the person who wants to be healthy so they can have a better home life, who better to hold them to account than their kids? This is a concept that I call inverting the hierarchy.

Many children will have been exposed to the concept when Mum or Dad draws a smiley face on a chart, often stuck to the fridge door, that highlights whether they've put their socks in the wash basket, done their homework, etc. By inventing the hierarchy, the parent is just asking the child to do the same for them.

Draw up an accountability chart for you, make it visible, and then ask your children or partner, or whoever your goal will impact the most, to provide the feedback. They will be holding you responsible for your actions and the emotional attachment will become a powerful driver for change.

What Dad got up to this week

	Mon	Tue	Wed	Thu	Fri	Sat	Sun
Exercise	☺		☺			☺	
Home on time	☺	☺	☹	☹	☺		
Get to the park				☹			☺
No phone at the table	☺	☺	☹	☹	☺	☺	☺

Example of an accountability chart

CASE STUDY – HITTING THE WALL

This case study looks at a national lead in a global business. They had spent the last decade throwing themselves into their work and little else. To use their words, they told me 'I feel as if I have hit the wall'. The data below represents a twenty-four-hour period and shows why the person was feeling low on energy – their quality of sleep is very poor.

Stress and recovery chart

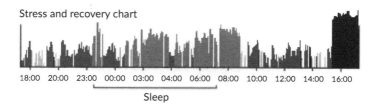

16:00 18:00 20:00 23:00 00:00 03:00 04:00 06:00 08:00 10:00 12:00 14:00

Sleep

We talked about many things, but one question in particular seemed to unlock a new behaviour. I simply asked, 'What do you love doing?'

They thought, and after some deliberation, responded, 'Roller skating.' Then I was treated to a monologue extolling the freedom, the fresh air, the scenery and all the other wonders that came with this activity, a narrative that clearly inspired this person.

My next question was, 'When did you last do this?'

'Around eight months ago.'

We talked and hatched a plan that provided them with the belief that it was OK to look after themselves. Roller skating would resume!

When monitored six weeks later, the improvement in their data, in particular their sleep, was immense.

Stress and recovery chart

18:00 20:00 23:00 00:00 03:00 04:00 06:00 08:00 10:00 12:00 14:00 16:00

Sleep

The short-term benefit to this person's wellbeing is clear to see, but what the data doesn't tell is that eight months later they were promoted to a global lead role. Yes, exercise is likely to improve the quality of your health and your balance, but I would suggest that doing something you love also has an important role to play in improving your work-life.

The last message in this section is simple – looking after yourself can also mean looking after business.

SECTION 3

THE SECOND GOAL: YOU AND YOUR WORK

Consistently winning in a team environment is rarely achieved through ability alone. Good teams have talent, but great teams have a shared purpose and a magnetic leader.

Over the past three decades, I have witnessed many styles of leadership. Whether they are the coach of a professional sports team, the CEO of a multinational organisation or a consultant in charge of a medical unit, these leaders' dominant and often career-defining traits vary considerably. Some demonstrate exceptional tactical acumen, some demand an ethic of hard work, others seek harmony through consensus, while one or two may have relied on ruling through fear.

Whatever the leader's style, leadership has an impact on output. Get it wrong and, at both an individual and organisational level, the gifted may start to underperform; get it right and the average can surpass expectation.

This section looks at how you can work smarter and, in particular, how leaders and managers can be the multipliers for organisational effectiveness.

5
Leading In The Twenty-First Century

In the early and mid-part of the twentieth century, possibly due to the occurrence of two world wars, leadership was often determined by age, schooling or family line. The style was based on a hierarchical chain of command, and if a superior told you to do something, you did it. Rarely was a reason either given or a question asked. Organisational charts showed a unidirectional flow of traffic where the leader looked down and gave commands from a privileged viewpoint.

Things have changed. The connectivity of the worldwide web has provided us with a powerful platform for instantaneous interaction between multiple people in multiple locations at the mere click of a button. The traditional top-down line of communication, where the leader sits at the tip of the organisational arrow, is becoming impractical. The twenty-first century leader is having to learn how to guide from within – instead of being *the* team leader, they have found themselves becoming the leader of teams.

This changing model has seen a move away from a transactional style to one that is underpinned by understanding, balance and adaptability. With a new emphasis on transformation, the days of control and command are being replaced by coach and cajole.

Understanding

For your team to succeed, you need understanding in numerous dimensions. Not only will you need to seek clarity around the task that lies ahead and the actions required to achieve it, but you will also need to understand the nuances and traits of your team members.

Do you know what makes your people flourish at an individual level? Have you evaluated the personalities in your teams and thought through how they can gel? Are you clear on which relationships you will need to invest in? How will you ensure that the sum of the parts results in a multiplier effect rather than division and disharmony.

In the world of sport teams, the individuals that make up your own team can often be a bigger challenge than defeating the opposition. While in business considerable effort may be invested in the creation of a strategic plan, but making the time to understand those who will deliver it is often neglected – here the business has become its own worst enemy. If a two-way dialogue imbued with trust, authenticity and acceptance takes place, not only does the understanding increase, but so does the level of commitment to the cause.

Old style
- Controls
- One-way hierarchical push
- Team trusts the leader

New style
- Navigates
- Two-way communication
- Leader trusts the team

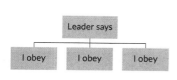

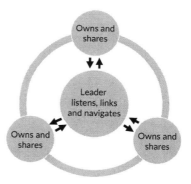

The changing face of leadership

Balance

The World Economic Forum outlines the top ten skills required to be successful in the working world of the 2020s as:

- Analytical thinking and innovation

- Active learning

- Complex problem solving

- Critical thinking

- Creativity, originality and initiative

- Leadership and social influence

- Technology use, monitoring and control

- Technology design and programming

- Resilience, stress tolerance and flexibility

- Reasoning, problem solving and ideation

To achieve many of these, you need to activate the pre-frontal cortex of the brain and utilise what are collectively known as the executive functions – problem solving, planning, paying attention, regulating emotions and decision making. These skills allow for greater integration between the intellectual, emotional and adaptive capabilities of the brain and are required to achieve a sense of balance.

As covered in Section 3, there are a range of ingredients on offer when it comes to staying energised. Successful leaders are likely to have developed a recipe that works for them, one that allows them to think clearly, communicate effectively and purvey a sense of calm.

Looking after others is important, and looking after yourself is in many ways the precursor for this. The example of putting your own oxygen mask on in an aeroplane before helping others is not new, but one that is relevant here.

Another area where balance is required is in evaluation. Organisations are particularly good at setting up inquiries, investigating errors and picking through poor performance with a fine-toothed comb when things have not gone well. It is right to reflect and learn from what has happened, but it is a shame that they don't apply a similar level of attention to detail in times of success.

The same is true in sport. The incriminating and soul-destroying reflection that occurs after a particularly humiliating loss tends to be way more detailed than the analysis of a fantastic victory.

If a team is firing on all cylinders, the balanced leader will look at the detail behind the good and encourage people to understand the factors that created the success. There will be a consistent approach in examining both the good and the bad.

Adaptability

In a world where things change at such a dramatic pace, the ability for an organisation to be agile is essential, as what is today's truth may well be tomorrow's lie. Intelligence quotient (IQ) has been recognised as important for many a year, emotional intelligence (EQ) has emerged more recently, but there is a new form of intelligence that I feel is becoming an essential skill for the modern-day leader, and that is adaptive intelligence (AQ).

There are many examples of businesses that have run into problems due to a lack of adaptability. The photograph printer who did not recognise the emergence of digital media can be bracketed with the retailer who failed to recognise the arrival of e-commerce. Their inability to adapt and evolve means they are now likely to be consigned to history.

Adaptability is not about reflex decisions that lurch the organisational ship in one direction and then another; it is having the ability to accept that change will happen and for the leader and their teams to understand that they may need to work with the change rather than fight against it.

A bit like a surfer, the leader will be looking for the right wave to catch. They are looking to be ahead of the crest with their eyes wide open, scouting for the perfect ride. If they take on too much, the surfer may crash and burn, and if they keep waiting for the perfect breaker, the competition may have disappeared off into the distance, never to be seen again. The great surfer is the one who adapts to the waves that are available to them; equally, the great leader is one who makes the best decisions. Neither can keep waiting forever.

Consequence analysis

Over my career, I have made some good decisions; I have also made some bad ones. Experience tells me that when several options are available or if doubt is lingering in my mind, there is benefit in pausing and performing something I refer to as a 'consequence analysis'.

A consequence analysis is a tool that, through logic, can provide the clarity of thinking that is required to evaluate the options, the risks and the alignment with your values. It simply leads to better decision making.

Here are the four steps of the consequence analysis:

Step 1 – make a list of the possibilities, and be sure to add not doing anything as one of the options. When you've done this, add notes on the impact each option will have on things that are important to you. People, profit and environment, factors that are sometimes referred to as the 'triple bottom line' are often popular, but you can add in other categories as you see fit (in the example below, you will see that 'brand' appears).

Step 2 – attribute a score between one and three for each option that relates to its impact, one being negative impact, two neutral and three positive.

Step 3 – specifically looks at how comfortable you feel with the risk involved with each option; it is not an evaluation of risk per se. One is uncomfortable, two acceptable and three comfortable.

Step 4 – once you have completed the scoring template, you may be drawn towards a particular option, but finish by evaluating whether it matches both the values of the company and your personal mission. If there is poor alignment, you may have taken the wrong path, or the values and vision of the organisation may need to be reviewed or – and this is often the hard one – you may need to hand the leadership baton on to someone else for the next stage of the corporate journey.

EXAMPLE – MOVING TO A NEW OFFICE

This example looks at a decision an organisation needed to make relating to a move to a new office. These were the three possibilities:

Option A: keep the whole team at the current central London standard venue (five-year lease; fixed rent; mutual break at three years; high cost per square foot).

Pros:

- Minimal disruption
- Whole team in one place

- Average location for all staff
- Known overhead

Cons:

- Long-term lease with no flexibility for expansion or contraction
- Poor location for some key staff
- Environment – old-fashioned and out of keeping with brand

Option B: move the whole team to a new central London venue (flexible office space; one-month notice period; high cost per square foot).

Pros:

- Flexible term of lease with short notice period allows for expansion/contraction
- Great environment that is in line with brand
- Good location for clients and all staff
- Whole team in one place

Cons:

- Significant increase in monthly overhead

Option C: split the team with some working in low-cost option in outer London and others working in a high-cost location in central London.

Pros:

- Medium risk on fixed costs
- Reduced space required for premium office space
- A range of locations to suit staff

Cons:

- Split venue could lead to divisions within the team
- Different environmental conditions for different people

	Option A		Option B		Option C		Do Nothing	
	Impact	Risk	Impact	Risk	Impact	Risk	Impact	Risk
People	2	2	1	2	3	2	1	2
Profit	2	2	3	1	2	2	2	2
Planet	1	2	1	2	2	3	1	2
Brand	1	2	3	3	2	3	1	2
Totals	6	8	7	8	6	10	5	8

The analysis, assuming finances, people and community are given equal weighting, suggested that for this organisation in this situation at this moment in time, the best option was C, and that doing nothing was likely to be less than ideal. This option is then tested against organisational values, and if there is alignment, that's the answer.

Adaptive communication

During my career, I have had my personality assessed in many ways: I have answered a series of questions and gained insights into both myself and how I interact with other people. One of the most useful assessments I underwent was a communication profiler that is simply known as Think, Feel, Know.[12] The premise for this is that we may all speak the same language, but we like to speak it and receive it in different ways. The assessment provides a view on your primary and secondary preferences and highlights the style that you are least likely to attach to.

Thinkers have a desire for detail, and lots of it. Their speech will be punctuated with facts and figures and their writing will be comprehensive and often populated with lists and multiple bullet points. They are happy to have conversations, that are typically lengthy and unconclusive, in a tone of voice that is likely to be stable in speed and tone. Their use of gesticulation or any other form of expressive body language will be minimal.

Feelers, on the other hand, have a desire for animation. Their language will be full of adverbs, adjectives and anecdotes. Their speech will vary in tone and pace, and they use body language and facial expressions liberally. They love an emotional approach that is full of energy and expression.

Knowers want to get straight to the point. They have no need for detail or description; they just want to get the conversations done and dusted. If they write an email, it is unlikely to contain any pleasantries, detail or emojis!

---

12 Clive Hyland, *Connect Through Think Feel Know* (Anoma Press Ltd, 2013)

Being aware of your preferred style is useful, but being able to detect the default style of others is powerful. Let's take the example of a car salesperson who has a primary preference to communicate in the style of think. If they are talking to a customer who is also think, then reeling off lists that relate to engine performance, on-sale value and boot capacity will lead to a good conversation as the thinking buyer will also want the sales process to be led by facts and figures.

If the salesperson uses the same approach with a knower, the success rate is likely to drop as their customer will simply be bored by the detail and disengage. The knower wants the purchase to be speedy. Equally, if the salesperson doesn't recognise a customer with a strong preference for the style of feel, they are missing a trick. The feeler will not be overly interested in the detail (unless, of course, it is embellished with descriptors); instead they will want a test drive, preferably with a friend, and they will be delighted by the sounds (stereo or engine) and enthused by the range of colours. The feeler will want the purchase to be an experience.

This is where the skill of adaptive communication can be so beneficial. If you can recognise the preferences of others and flex to their style, your influence and effectiveness will be multiplied.

There is one caveat to this in that personal preference may vary depending on the context of the conversation, so don't assume that the same person will always want to have a conversation in one specific style. You will have to use sense and make a judgement on what will work best at that particular moment in time.

Communication is a central part of our lives, and as a leader, you will often be judged by it. You can use style, body language and pace to punctuate the dialogue and create effective delivery, but remember that one of the most powerful elements to speech is the use of silence. Used in the right way and in the right place, silence can often have more influence than any words.

6
Motivation

You may be motivated by wealth, health, title, rank or maybe just common decency, but ultimately, motivation relates to the willingness to do something or be someone. And when it comes to creating that willingness across a group of people, it is likely that the leader will need to take on the mantle of motivator in chief.

Historically, motivation was initiated by those who demonstrated strength and resolve; people who were recognised for delivering deeds of derring-do. They were exemplars of all things to all people and often had titles that demonstrated just how good they were. Whether it be Alfred, Alexander or Catherine, their name was accompanied by 'The Great'.

Things have changed and I would suggest that the motivator of today has a range of tools that are far-reaching. They can nurture people, navigate problems, build on diversity and they ultimately create a sense of followership.

The art of motivation is particularly important for organisations that are either at the outset of their corporate journey or about to hit the turbulent times of change. Whether the road ahead is one of accelerated growth, merger, contraction or reinvention, these pivot points require a workforce that is committed.

The CRAFT of motivation

This commitment can be facilitated by five key traits that I refer to as the CRAFT of motivation.

Clarity

Not many people would board a ship if there was no information on where it was going and how long it would take. The same is true in the workplace. If you as leader don't provide clarity, then the workforce is unlikely to be engaged with the mission. Clarity does not equal certainty, but it does demonstrate competence and inspire confidence.

Relationships

To create followership, you need your people to understand you and you need to understand them. You will
have to invest time in developing relationships so you
can recognise people's motivating factors both at and
away from work.

Understanding people in the workplace is not as hard
as it may seem. Traditionally, people have been driven
by one of three factors. Money is the obvious one, but
not the only driver as some will desire a title, while
others will strive for peer recognition. Interestingly,
the Millennial generation has introduced the importance of social and environmental good and these are
further categories that should be considered.

As well as understanding what drives people at
work, having an insight into what energises someone away from work has merit. Take a hypothetical
example. Your finance director loves playing badmin-
ton; indeed, they are the stalwart of their local club
and have played matches there every Thursday night
for the past fifteen years. You decide that you want to
hold a finance meeting every other Thursday between
4 and 6pm. The obedient finance director will attend,
but at best is unlikely to be fully engaged and at worst
has probably spent the afternoon looking for other
jobs.

Through a lack of understanding, you have demotivated an important cog in your corporate machine. You may ask, 'How am I to know?' The answer to that is simple – invest time into building a relationship. If you don't know what is important to your team members outside work, it means you simply have not had the conversation.

Authenticity

If your goal is to motivate people, the more human you can be yourself, the greater connection you are likely to experience. Audiences tend to be rather good at sniffing out nonsense, so authenticity and, potentially, vulnerability are key attributes to demonstrate.

When mentoring physiotherapists, I listen to how they answer questions that are presented by patients. A question such as 'What is wrong with my knee?' is perfectly reasonable, but sometimes the physiotherapist won't know the answer. That is no slight on the therapist as knee conditions can be complex, but in the early stages of their career, I often hear them waffling themselves into trouble rather than simply looking the patient in the eye and saying, 'I am not 100% sure, but let's find out'.

This approach does not abdicate responsibility; instead the honesty, put alongside an attitude that takes ownership of what happens next, provides way more confidence and belief in patients than a therapist who tries to bluff their way through a treatment. The same is true when you're leading a business. Balance confidence and strength with vulnerability and authenticity.

Fairness

One rule for one and one for another is probably the best way to create division. Whether it relates to gender, race, religion or pay, a lack of parity is unlikely to be tolerated and, as shown by campaigns such as #MeToo and Black Lives Matter, will be unacceptable to your people and your clients. Simply put, a lack of fairness is bad for business and brand, and in the long run is likely to be bad for you too.

Thank you

One of the leading researchers into positive psychology is behavioural economist, Dan Ariely, who has done a range of experiments that demonstrate why personalising appreciation is important. In one of his studies, Ariely gave three groups of students a sheet of paper and asked them to identify pairs of identical letters. Once they had completed a sheet, they were offered some money, but the reward was reduced as the task progressed.

Those in the first group were asked to write their name at the top of the piece of paper, and when they handed in their work, it was looked over, acknowledged and placed in a pile. Those in the second group did not write their name, nor did they receive any acknowledgement before their sheets of paper were placed in a pile. Those in the third group would see their work shredded as soon as it was handed in.

Unsurprisingly, the results showed that those whose work was shredded needed nearly double the amount of money as those who had received recognition if the task was to be repeated. A similar impact was seen when Ariely looked at the second group. Even though their work was not destroyed, the lack of personal appreciation resulted in them demanding an increased tariff to continue the task. Those in group one, whose work was accompanied by acknowledgement, ended up doing more for less.[13]

'Thank you' are two words that make a difference, but if you want to make a greater impact, add a name and some context.

CRAFT is also a useful model to use when you're looking at self-motivation. Are you **clear** in what you want to achieve? Have you evaluated the **relationship** impact with those you love? Are you being **authentic** to your underlying values? Are you being **fair** to yourself? And when was the last time you were **thankful** for… well, just being you?

---

13   Dan Ariely, *Payoff: The hidden logic that shapes our motivations* (Simon and Schuster, 2016)

Take a holistic approach to appraisals

Historically, the main objective of an appraisal was to understand the effectiveness of an employee, identify areas where they could improve and put in place a plan that, more than anything, focused on how the employee could help the company be more productive and profitable. Goals would be identified, actions agreed and targets set. Occasionally, appraiser and appraisee would discuss the benefits, though rarely did these go beyond how achievement of the goal might lead to financial reward.

Things are changing. Relying on a once-yearly appraisal does not align itself with the agility required to flourish in a rapidly changing world. The alternative is to create a living document that evolves throughout the year and acts as an ongoing reference point. This requires the commitment to create the time to talk on a regular basis: weekly may be too often, quarterly too little, so monthly may be a good starting point. Your style may be driven by structure or it can be open-ended, but ideally, deliver the session in a way that is agreeable to the person you are talking to, so do remember to adapt your communication style (see Chapter 5).

If you are looking for a methodical approach, you may find the example below useful. You will see that I have consistently used the phrase 'how can *we* help' – this is important as if you always ask 'how can *I* help?', you're likely to find that you have increased your workload considerably. The use of 'we' emphasises the concept of team and mutual responsibility.

EXAMPLE – APPRAISAL QUESTIONS

While you don't need to ask every question in every appraisal, you may wish to consider these:

How is work going and how can we help?

- Explore whether the person is doing the job that you (and they) think they should be doing. Is there alignment with their job description? If not, should this be amended?

- Review any learning the person has done and ask whether it has been helpful, and if so, how they are using it. And remember to check in on how they are dealing with technology advances.

- Relationships are important, so add in a direct question about the person's interactions with other team members and leaders.

- Fairness – whether it be pay, hours or demands, do not duck this question. You can ask it in a direct and closed fashion, eg 'Do you feel you are being treated fairly at the moment?', or more openly, eg 'What are your feelings about work at the moment?'

How is life going and how can we help?

- Ask how energised the person feels and what factors are leading to that score.

- Family and relationships – it is not just about partner and children; for several people, the biggest challenge can be elderly relatives.

- Ask how balanced they feel life is. What is going well and what is missing?

Do you have a long-term plan and how can we help?

- It doesn't matter if the answer is yes or no, but it is useful to show that you care about the bigger picture. If you discover that someone wants to travel around the world in the next couple of years, you'll know they're unlikely to be working with you for much longer – you may also gain some insight into your future staffing needs.

This format will not work for everyone and every organisation. Some people find it hard to open up about life away from work; they may feel that it is none of your business. That is fine; respect their view and privacy. The important thing is to offer genuine interest and ask the right questions. The increasing desire for more in life than just work, particularly from the Millennial generation and younger, means that the concept of work-life integration as opposed to separation needs to be evaluated, coached and demonstrated.

Once the appraisal document is completed, it can be used as a reference point and amended as the months progress. The more holistic and adaptive your approach, the greater the insights you will gain. Done well, it will allow you to be more effective as the creator of cohesion between your people and the factors that could enable them to navigate the challenges of work and home more effectively.

Stop wasting time

Meetings

Whether they are face to face, virtual, one to ones, team, planning, reviewing, strategising or back to back, meetings seem to dominate the working lives of many. Yet when they're asked to articulate their feelings towards these get-togethers, people's dialogue rarely overflows with enthusiasm. What was that all about? Why was I there? I really do have better things to do. All these thoughts can cross the minds of the attendees as the chair closes proceedings.

How can you ensure that attendees at your meetings have a sense of purpose on arrival, and that they are energised and enthused for action on departure? The first thing to ensure is that you get the basics right:

- **Agenda.** An agenda that is copied and pasted week in, week out will become white noise and likely to be ignored. If you want to evaluate the attention that people pay to those weekly bullet points, this simple experiment may help: replace one of the usual items, eg 'Financial Update', with 'A Visit from Coco the Clown' and see how many people notice. The number is likely to be less than 50%.

  Create an agenda that has interest. For example, 'Financial Update' could become 'How we have hit our cost-saving targets for March'. You could also use a motivational statement at the top of the agenda. Even a different font or colour is likely to grab greater attention.

- **Pre-meeting papers.** Submit these to the attendees at least forty-eight hours before the meeting if you want people to have the chance to read and reflect on them.

- **Space.** Mix up the locations for your meetings or, if this is not possible, ask people to change where they sit. If you are having a meeting of fewer than thirty minutes, consider no chairs – stand and talk. If nothing else, the meeting is likely to conclude in the allotted time.

- **Devices.** There will be some occasions when there is benefit in people taking digital notes or referencing papers; there will be others when attendees having a laptop open, disengaging from the meeting and doing their own thing is downright rude. As a basic rule, if the meeting is based on fact and intellect, then allow devices; if the topic is sensitive or has an emotional undercurrent, then don't. If the chairperson states at the start of the meeting whether it is a laptop open or closed session, people know where they stand.

- **Walk and talk.** A good way to hold a one-to-one meeting is to walk and talk outdoors. Aside from the obvious benefits of exercise and daylight, there can be other pluses. The side-to-side body position naturally reduces eye contact, the physical barrier of a face-to-face encounter across a desk is eliminated and you have created a less intense environment.

- **Timing.** Too many meetings either start late, run over or run out of time. If one person turns up ten minutes late and there are six people attending, it doesn't take a genius to work out that an hour has been lost by the collective.

  If your organisation has a culture of back-to-back meetings and you feel that you never have time to reflect on the proceedings you have just attended, experiment with start and end times. One method that seems to work is instead of sixty-minute chunks, look at a standard time of forty minutes. Start at ten past the hour and finish at ten to the hour, and you have reclaimed 33% of your time – time that may be useful for reflecting and acting on all the things you and your colleagues have been discussing. It is also likely that you will have achieved in forty minutes what you thought would take an hour.

- **Respect the full agenda.** How often does item one on the agenda get 90% of the meeting time, and then items two, three, four and five are squeezed into ten minutes? A meeting that overruns may suit you, but how is that impacting on everyone else in the room? A 'time monitor' (ideally not the chairperson) can help police the pace and ensure that each item receives equal attention.

- **Energy.** Sometimes, a meeting is required to go on all day. If this is the case, think how you can maintain the energy across the group. Regular breaks, hydration, movement and fresh air will all help, as will creating clear focus around what the meeting will look to cover in the next hour. Do not let the meeting or the energy drift.

- **Chairperson.** Chairing is a skill underpinned by efficiency and calm. If these traits are not your forte, you can benefit from finding an alternate. Equally, there may be some meetings where there is benefit in the leader contributing as a participant rather than adopting the neutrality of the chair.

- **The right people for the right occasion.** If agendas can adapt, then so too can the participants. Too often, the wrong people are in the wrong place at the wrong time. It is always possible that someone's time would be better spent elsewhere, so remember that as long as good communications are in place (minutes, conversations or even a recording of a Zoom session), absence in person does not mean exclusion from the meeting.

Email and communication platforms

If the enthusiasm for meetings is low, I have yet to come across an organisation where the feeling towards email, WhatsApp, Yammer or Slack is any better. These digital tools provide great communication possibilities that should lead to increased productivity, but the way organisations often insist on using them can lead to anger and the occasional expletive being aimed at a screen.

There are many ways to master the minutia of effective digital communication, but I want to highlight a couple of factors that, in some ways, could be considered cultural.

A lack of knowledge around how to use tech can lead to frustration, especially if there are inconsistent capabilities across the organisation. Technological competency should not be assumed and ensuring people are comfortable with things should be an ongoing process. Effective training can resolve this, and as technology advances at such a rapid rate, do not think that everyone's knowledge is the same as yours. It may be lesser; equally it may be more advanced and you might be a source of frustration.

The second problem relates to the habits of people whose behaviours may not be entirely in line with the corporate message. 'We really respect that you have a life away from work, holidays are important and balance and energy are good for you' is the sort of mantra that leaders often spout, yet their own actions do not match their dialogue.

If you send out emails late at night, it is possible that those around you may feel they should be responding at a similar hour. If the cc tab is heavily populated, the problem becomes contagious and you have an organisational culture that is constantly switched on.

Sending a message 'out of hours' can cause angst, but is the problem solely with the sender? The answer is probably no. Take, for example, a manager who has had to accompany their partner to a hospital appointment in the afternoon. They may have seen messages arriving while sitting in the waiting room, yet they decided to give their attention to their loved one rather than their phone.

On arriving back home, late in the evening, the manager starts responding to the digital traffic that has mounted up. They could write their response and program when it is sent (if they have the technical competency to do this) or they could just send them out that evening. The latter is fine as long as a conversation around email engagement has taken place – hopefully one that has stated it is okay to send but recipients are expected to read and respond at an appropriate time.

Creating a culture that supports the effective use of time and technology is important if organisational energy is to be conserved.

Evaluate

The last point I want to make about addressing both meetings and emails is that too many conversations are based solely on emotion. I am usually an advocate for the articulation of feelings; they shouldn't be ignored, but occasionally it's more useful to reflect on the facts. If you feel that email is getting out of hand, take a moment to evaluate how many emails you receive. How many are you cc'd in to? What percentage of these do you feel are important, useful or relevant?

Similarly, don't just evaluate how many meetings you have, it is useful to match that statistic with a view on output. Use the template below to see how effective you are being with your time and energy.

	Monday		Tuesday		Wednesday		Thursday		Friday	
	a.m.	p.m.	a.m.	p.m.	a.m.	p.m.	a.m.	p.m.	a.m.	p.m.
Hours in meetings										
Value of meetings										
Personal effectiveness										
Personal energy										
Team effectiveness										
Team energy										

Both meetings and digital communications are an inevitable part of working life, so spending a moment to understand how you are using your time and drawing up guidelines for future working practice is highly beneficial if you are looking to increase personal effectiveness.

Creating a time-effective culture

Whether it be meetings or email, what worked for you may not be perfect for others so beware dictating a policy. Instead, use a range of people to create a consensus. If you are a dominant force within the organisation, you may have to show some vulnerability to give others the confidence to contribute.

Here are some ideas on starting the conversation.

An opening gambit of 'I don't think meetings are working, what do you think we should do?' is unlikely to stimulate open conversation in the same way as 'I am not sure I have got meetings right recently, and sometimes find myself feeling a little flat afterwards. Are you OK to provide three ideas that you think would make our meetings more energised?' By using language that reflects your feeling rather than your thinking, you are showing greater authenticity and giving people permission to contribute. This subtle change is likely to engage people and encourage them to work with you, rather than leaving them feeling they have yet another chore to complete.

Once the ideas are in, discuss them as a group, agree upon the best way forward, and then look to conduct an experiment. Experiments are great to run in a corporate organisation – they are neither a policy nor a procedure, but a way of exploring best future practice. They can fail, be rerun or discarded, but above all, they do not put excessive pressure on the creation of perfection at the first time of asking.

From discussion to implementation, review and conclusion, it is important to set a timeframe and continually re-engage with all the people who are contributing to the process. These things often start with a bang of enthusiasm, only to peter out long before they reach the finishing line.

Once you have run the experiment, your meetings could be a roaring success. It is possible you may need to make some tweaks; and there is always a chance that the experiment will fail to achieve its objectives. Whatever the outcome, never regard an experiment as a waste of time – it is simply a learning process.

Values and Mission

Companies spend considerable time, effort and money in identifying the beliefs and behaviours that they would like to be at the core of their corporate DNA. These characteristics are drawn together, a list of values is cited and, when put alongside a mission statement, the way a business lives and breathes is articulated to its people, its customers and, in the case of some of the large global brands, the world.

A few years ago, I noted down a selection of values statements:

- 'Respect, excellence, safety, courage and one team' was the mantra of an energy firm

- 'Pride, achievement, respect, innovation and care' were the foundations for an NHS Trust

- 'Respect, integrity, service, excellence, stewardship' were the pillars for a major bank

The similarity in tone made me wonder how important these statements are. When working with teams, in addition to asking them if they can recall the words (for most this can be a struggle), I also ask them to articulate exactly what they actually mean to them (for many this causes a stumbling silence).

If you look again at the examples listed, you will see the word 'respect' is repeated in all three. Does this word mean the same thing in each environment? I suspect there may well be some differences, and this demonstrates how useful it is to create clarity and provide meaning in straight-forward language – not everyone will interpret the same word in the same way.

Another benefit of providing a description is that a certain sense of realism and balance can be introduced. For example, if you state that one of your values is 'Perfect', you may want to add some narrative that starts with *'our goal is'* or *'we aspire to be'*. This moves a one-word dream to a realistic ambition, and in a world where cynicism can sometimes reign supreme it can provide some leeway if things don't quite go to plan.

EXAMPLE – CLARITY OF MEANING IN MISSION AND VALUES

In 2010 FIFA, an organisation with the remit to oversee the governance of the most popular sport in the world, articulated their mission as:

'We see it as our mission to contribute towards building a better future for the world by using the power and popularity of football. This mission gives meaning and direction to each and every activity that FIFA is involved in – football being an integrated part of our society.'

The statement was accompanied with the following values:

Authenticity – we believe that football must remain a simple, beautiful game played by, enjoyed by and touching the lives of all people far and wide.

Unity – we believe it is FIFA's responsibility to foster unity within the football world and to use football to promote solidarity regardless of gender, ethnic background, faith, or culture.

Performance – we believe that FIFA must strive to deliver football of the highest quality and as the best quality experience, be it as a player, as a spectacle or as a major cultural or social enabler throughout the world.

Integrity – we believe that, just as the game itself, FIFA must be a model of fair play, tolerance, sportsmanship and transparency.[14]

The sentiments are good and the explanations clear, but history suggests that, across the organisation, some of the words may not have been universally matched with aligned actions. The allegations made against some of the leadership at FIFA are well documented.[15] It is a shame that the way the organisation's dialogue has evolved has not received quite so much coverage.

Ten years on and the vision for FIFA is now stated as:

'To promote the game of football, protect its integrity and bring the game to all.'

Instead of values, this is accompanied by an updated list of guiding principles:

- **Transparency** – FIFA will be transparent in how it governs and grows the game, operates its business and interacts with key stakeholders.

---

14 David Rowe, 'Arrivals hall message: Global media, global sport', *Global Media Sport: Flows, Forms and Futures* (London: Bloomsbury Academic, 2011). http://dx.doi.org/10.5040/9781849661577.ch-001
15 BBC News, 'Fifa corruption crisis: key questions answered', BBC News, 2015. www.bbc.co.uk/news/world-europe-32897066

- **Accountability** – FIFA will be held accountable by football stakeholders around the globe – particularly member associations.

- **Inclusivity** – FIFA will reflect the world and the communities in which it operates.

- **Cooperation** – FIFA will actively engage with football's diverse ecosystem to shape the future of football.[16]

The current iteration is much more inward-looking; it seems to have a greater focus on the organisation rather than the world. I suspect that FIFA now has much greater connectivity between its vision, values and actions.

In summary, creating a mission statement, articulating a vision or listing a set of values all have their place, ensuring they are understood and delivered by all – which is probably way more important.

Culture and anti-culture

Famed management consultant Peter Drucker coined the phrase 'Culture eats strategy for breakfast', and who am I to argue with that? What I would like to add is that the anti-cultures may eat culture for lunch, dinner and possibly even afternoon tea.

---

16   FIFA, 'Our strategy', FIFA. www.fifa.com/who-we-are/explore-fifa

Whereas values are thought of as the foundation stones of an organisation, culture can be thought of as the heartbeat. Defined as the behavioural traits that exist between a group of people, culture is the day-to-day pulse that provides an insight into a team's underlying cohesion.

When your culture is buoyant, your team members will have pride in the brand. There will be respect and camaraderie between employees, who will be focused, energised and engaged. Attrition of key people is likely to be minimal.

When the culture is bad, teams become dysfunctional, unproductive and fatigued. You as a leader will spend all your energy firefighting, replacing staff and asking yourself, 'Why do I bother?' Welcome to the world of the anti-culture.

Addressing your anti-cultures is just as important as identifying your cultural drivers. The method I am going to share for creating a culture code is modified from a technique that I was introduced to by a South African organisation which used a combination of pictures, words and mathematics to produce art that articulates culture. Aside from the creativity and beautifully produced imagery used to represent its raison d'être, it was the first time I had seen the portrayal of the negative factors that could impact a business. They had delivered a balanced approach that addressed both the good and the bad. When working on culture,

I use some of these ideas, and particularly imagery, to unlock conversations across a team.

The following process might be useful to follow if addressing the culture/anti-culture conundrum with a team. Initially split people into small groups and provide each group with an identical pack of cards. On each card, a trait is described by both a word and picture – I typically use a pack that outlines 100+ themes.

Some of the pictures are associated with positive behaviours, eg caring, thorough, grateful. Some are negative, eg cynical, disorganised, aloof. A few themes may be interpreted as either a positive or negative trait, eg risk averse – something that may be important to a health and safety team, but a significant barrier to progress for the creatives.

Each of the groups works its way through the cards and ends up by choosing the five factors they think underpin successful team dynamics. I call these the drivers. They will also identify the five factors they consider to be a hindrance, these are known as the drainers. Each group will then talk through its choices before starting a filtration process that leaves them in agreement on the five key drivers and five key drainers. These factors will become the skeleton for the organisation's cultural code.

However, the skeleton needs fleshing out and the exercise does not finish with the simple agreement around words and pictures. There are two further steps to complete. The first is to ask the groups to create a clear understanding of what each word means to them and ensure the collective agrees on a definition. The next step is for them to note down a real-life example of each specific trait, ideally one that is relevant to their team. Only once this is completed can you draw up a culture code document.

If you look to do this, be aware that it can take some time. Even across a closely-knit team, it is highly likely there will be a range of opinions and lively debate should be seen and encouraged.

The example below is one that was created by the support staff at a professional sports club. The creation took around three hours and involved five people. It stimulated robust discussion and, as a process, helped realign the team with what the members wanted to achieve and how they were interacting with each other.

Creating a culture code is just the start. The document's content needs to be reviewed and people held accountable for its delivery. If it's not revisited and discussed regularly, the chance of disengagement will increase and old habits can return.

Drivers	Drainers
Trust We will be confident that we are all doing things for the right reason and back each and every member of the team. Additionally, we will do our utmost to build trust with players, coaches and club.	**Poor Communication** We will avoid inconsistent messages that lack clarity and specificity; we will communicate to the right people, at the right time, and if we are unsure, we will ask.
Consistent We will look to provide high standards of cover, service and progressive thinking to ALL teams that come under our remit.	**Shackled** We will introduce new ideas to benefit players, club and our team. These may revolve around processes, procedures, communication, research and development.
Teamwork We will support each other to deliver our roles with energy, focus and purpose and ensure we are stronger as a group, as opposed to being a group of individuals.	**Disorganised** We will abide by the systems and processes designed to provide a professional service underpinned by diligence and governance.
Innovation We want to be ahead of the pack as a sports science & medicine team. We do not 'Keep up with the Joneses'; we are the Joneses.	**Scattergun** We will play to our strengths, utilising our individual skills to maximise benefit to player and club.
Personal Development We will foster an environment where personal development is encouraged through either formal or experiential learning and explore a range of environments.	**Free Radical** We will act as a team and, regardless of personal agenda, ambition or intellectual disagreement, we will demonstrate unity.

Sample drivers and drainers (excluding pictures)

Following the creation, individuals were asked to provide a score (one to five) on how well they thought the collective had done in demonstrating each of the positive traits and avoiding each of the negative ones. The review was repeated monthly and ensured that the team worked on delivering the culture it wanted. The output was a greater sense of togetherness; one where an appreciation for individuals increased within the immediate team and also across the whole organisation.

Culture and diversity

Culture is not something that can be dictated; it comes from within and is developed by a group of people who have the trust to articulate a version that is right for them at a specific moment in time. While the values should be consistent across an organisation, culture is more dynamic and can differ from team to team – the ideal heartbeat in sales is likely to be different to the pulse that is required in finance.

It may be useful to think of culture as part of your approach to diversity. Encourage your teams to accept that they can be different, so long as they are getting the job done.

CASE STUDY – A DOCTOR'S DRIVERS AND DRAINERS

The idea of drivers and drainers can also be used to evaluate personal satisfaction in a job. Let's have a look at data that covers a day in the life of a doctor who works at a teaching hospital. Part of their job involves seeing patients, while the remainder of their time is spent as a research fellow.

The data shows a day when the doctor's morning task was in the laboratory, while they spent the afternoon seeing patients. It is clear that this doctor is more at ease in the research environment than a clinical setting.

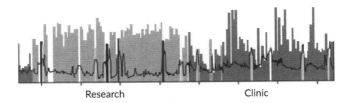

Research   Clinic

When the doctor saw the data, they were initially surprised, but as our conversation developed, it started to make sense to them. The doctor talked about their research with enthusiasm, but when they were talking about the clinic, their energy dampened as they expressed their frustration.

The doctor was at a point in their career when doing clinical work was a non-negotiable, but the data helped them think through a couple of things. Firstly, how could they make the clinics less draining? The doctor decided that while they couldn't change having to do the clinic, they could invest in improving their relationships with the administration staff, who are essential in the smooth running of the session. Secondly, it reinforced the doctor's future professional direction of travel and affirmed their underlying desire to search out a post where research dominated.

As we bring this section to a close and reflect on how the world of leadership in a work setting has changed, let's now turn our attention to the wider community. There's a big, wide world out there and we all have a place in it.

SECTION 4

THE THIRD GOAL:
YOU AND YOUR WORLD

At the start of the 2020s, we witnessed an unprecedented global pandemic. The foothills of the new decade have not been friendly and the first steps, like so many other journeys, have been hard ones to take. But amid the misery, one of the few positives to emerge has been a greater appreciation for the concept of community, something that for many has been a lost aspect of life.

Many people across the UK gathered on their doorsteps to clap for the NHS and other key workers, but there are many others who deserve praise for the way they provided support. Whether they were the home-based sewing machinists who started to manufacture protective equipment for frontline medical staff, the volunteers who appeared in their masses to run errands for those that were housebound, the teachers who delivered virtual classes or my neighbour, Nicholas, who helped resuscitate my car battery on a damp April morning, the examples of people wanting to help others in this time of great need have been considerable. In general, there has been a resurgence in humanity and humility as people started to feel increasingly vulnerable.

Community is back in fashion. The question is, will this be a wave that has the power to knock over barriers and provide long-lasting influence, or will it be one that teases, and simply provides a moment of enthusiasm before retreating back into the abyss of an undefined ocean?

The aim of this section is to challenge you to think about the benefits of community – *your* world rather than *the* world – and consider how you interact with it. To claim a scoreline of 3–0 in your battle for balance, you must go beyond self-improvement actions, push your thinking way further than just your business, and consider how you can positively interact with your community, too.

7
What Is A Community?

Most people are positive about the word 'community'. They want to help it, be part of it and build it. But what exactly is a community? Does the word describe the 2,748 people you have arbitrarily connected with on a social media platform? Is it the affinity you share with the fellow supporters of your favourite football club? Is it an affiliation you have with other members of your professional body? Is it something that is defined by geographical borders? Or are you connected by religion, sexuality or another demographical marker?

The word 'community' reaches far and wide. It is one of those words that can mean pretty much anything, yet often amounts to nothing. There is no right or wrong, but tightening up the definition of your community may be useful when you think about how you will interact with it.

There are several ways you may engage with a community, but broadly speaking, you can either give to it, support it or be with it. None of these interactions is bad; in fact, they are all great and can often co-exist, but it is important to understand that scoring the third goal and achieving great balance occurs through being part of a community.

Community giving

Community giving relates to pounds and pennies, a financial transaction that is made either by an individual or an organisation. A key catalyst for community giving occurred in 1985 when Sir Bob Geldof staged the Live Aid concerts in London and Philadelphia. Moved by the poverty and starvation in Ethiopia, Geldof brought together an array of stars from the world of music and put on a show, televised to millions, the like of which had never been seen before.

While the event was spectacular, it was the emotional pleas and the use of film to portray the poverty that pulled at the heart strings of so many people. Delivered in a concentrated timeframe, the message was raw, challenging and gnawed away at the conscience; suddenly, charity was not just a cake sale or a village fete, it was emotional and it was in your face. The wallets of the masses opened up and the event raised an estimated $125 million.

Giving to good causes was not new, but for so many people to give over such a short period of time definitely was, and it was not just wallets that were unlocked. Live Aid created a template for events such as Children in Need and Comic Relief, and significantly changed the landscape of the third sector.

Community supporting

Supporting your community is typically done through either knowledge or actions. You may be an accountant who is happy to give up some time to help oversee the finances of your child's youth club, or you may be someone who volunteers to be a marshal at the local parkrun. This form of interaction is no longer about money; the commodities have become time and knowledge.

While community supporting is often demonstrated at an individual level, it is gaining popularity in the corporate sector. With the increasing expectation for organisations to deliver a social responsibility programme, companies are starting to complement financial giving with the donation of time. Examples include committing a team of people to tidy up the local park or offering to paint the hospice day centre.

These actions are clearly good for the park or hospice. Equally, they are likely to bond people together, improve engagement and can be used for brand promotion. Corporate community supporting is definitely a win-win.

Community being

The investment of time and money is straightforward; the concept of 'being' is more nebulous, and as such is one that is tougher to explain. Fabian Pfortmüller, co-founder of the Together Institute, makes a good observation when he suggests that for all the dialogue around shared interest, purpose, intent and togetherness, if a fully trusting relationship is not present, then the soul of the community is absent.[17] My view is that while community being may still involve money and time, it is centred around a group of people who have a common sense of purpose and a mutual emotional attachment. They are bound by reliability, confidence, acceptance and, possibly even, safety.

Community being is something that makes you solid on the outside and smile on the inside.

---

17   Fabian Pfortmüller. 'What does "community" even mean? A definition attempt and conversation starter', The Together Institute, 2017. https://medium.com/together-institute/what-does-community-even-mean-a-definition-attempt-conversation-starter-9b443fc523d0

EXAMPLE – A CRICKETING COMMUNITY

In 2005, I moved out of London and headed 20 miles north to the city of St Albans. There are many ways to integrate with the local community, but when your children are nine and six, the school playground is an obvious starting point. I soon discovered the existence of a dads' cricket team that sold itself as a collection of gentleman, players and useful chaps.

The Garden Fields School Dads CC, or Men of Fields as they like to be known, turned out at least once a week and played matches against other school-inspired teams. The cricket was poor, I was poor, but there were two factors that made this so enjoyable.

The first was the venue. Verulamium Park provides an appalling pitch that is peppered with rabbit droppings, but surrounded by a collection of magnificent trees and overlooked by St Albans Abbey, it is a beautiful place to spend a summer's evening. The second was the camaraderie: a post-match visit to the pub furthered the bond, and activities such as golf days and Christmas parties were a great way to meet new people and settle into a local community. Happy days.

During my first season, one of the members was diagnosed with pancreatic cancer, and two years later, he passed away, leaving a wife and daughter. He died aged forty-one. Inevitably, there was a sense of loss, but the community rallied and offered to help the family in the way that is typically seen in times of grief. But what was interesting was that this rallying, unlike so many others, didn't dissipate and disappear after a while – if anything, it grew.

A decade on and the group continues to play cricket and socialise, but the greater purpose now revolves around supporting each other, our families and the community. We have a collective realisation that being part of this community is, in some ways, an insurance policy – if something happens to me, I know that there will be a group of people out there who will help as well as they can.

When I think about why this group of cricketing dads continues to do so much, I am drawn to a couple of possibilities. First, human beings enjoy giving. While good deeds help others, they make the giver feel good, too.

The second possibility is that the death of our friend at such a young age highlighted just how vulnerable we all are. For some, it was a catalyst for a visible and major shift in their personal lives; for others, the impact was less obvious; but for all, the event underlined the importance of togetherness.

And finally, as we have seen a pandemic highlight the importance of using gloves, masks and sanitiser, and promote health through diet and exercise, we should consider the concept of psychosocial immunity. Love and laughter can increase our level of lymphocytes, blood cells that are important to our immune system; so if we are looking for an additional layer of protection against an aggressive virus, it may be worth exploring our community being.

A community is complex

Just before the end of the twentieth century, strategic thinker David Snowden introduced the Cynefin model.[18] The framework, named after the Welsh word for habitat, helps us consider not just the challenge that lies in front of us, but our interaction with it. It also suggests that this should vary depending on whether the problem is simple, complicated, complex or chaotic.

A simple challenge is one where proven knowledge and order prevail – if you follow the rule, then you will find the answer. The thought process revolves around straightforward categorisation and the application of established logic. A mathematical calculation is a good example. By applying a process such as brackets, orders, division, multiplication, addition, subtraction (BODMAS), we determine the solution by following basic rules rather than any form of lateral thinking.

A complicated challenge is one where multiple processes need to be brought together to achieve the best result. Building a car may seem to be incredibly tricky, but if the various tasks are followed in the right order, the end product is likely to be a fully functional vehicle where the different components of engineering

---

18 David Snowden and Mary Boone, 'A leader's framework for decision making', *Harvard Business Review*, 2007. https://hbr.org/2007/11/a-leaders-framework-for-decision-making

work in harmony. Here the thought process revolves around analysing and integrating a number of steps.

A complex challenge is one where the random nature of human beings comes into play and the emotional layer that often bubbles underneath the surface needs to be appreciated. When we're faced with a problem that involves people, it is worth taking the time to probe and explore, draw on our emotional intelligence and aim to understand the feelings rather than solely focusing on facts, rules or technical requirements.

Finally, there are some problems, often involving human beings, that are not accompanied by the luxury of time, and these can be thought of as chaos. If a child is having a meltdown in the middle of a supermarket, we might not consider it the right place or time to probe and explore the reasons why. This challenge needs immediate action.

EXAMPLE – BREXIT

For those living in the community that is known as the United Kingdom, the challenge of delivering Brexit dominated the news from June 2016 to the start of the new decade. It is a useful way to demonstrate how an inability to differentiate the complicated from the complex can lead to a shambolic mess. It is also a great example of how not to deal with a challenge.

If we rewind the clock to the immediate aftermath of the referendum. Leave had 51.89% of the vote, and

Brexit supporters celebrated while the 48.11% who wished to remain part of the European Union found themselves in the depths of despair. In the world of the simple problem solver, Brexit was a done deal.

Of course, we all know that this result was far from simple, and that the kingdom was most definitely not united. Over the following three years, the public lived through an arduous process of negotiation that was primarily based on law, facts and figures. The approach focused on understanding technicalities – get that right and everything would be sorted. The method of addressing the challenge had moved from the simple to the complicated, the assumption being that while there was disagreement, it would be the law books that would provide the answers. How wrong could people be?

Remainers abhorred any form of progress while leavers would resist a backward step. Deals were haggled over, draft agreements would flit back and forward between Brussels and London, but progress was negligible because the country's leaders were treating the problem like a piece of machinery and forgetting that inside the machine there were people – people who had a voice. The harder politicians tried to find a resolution, the more entrenched the public became in their views – it was the logjam of all logjams. The arguments had moved from the intellect and were now being fuelled by hearts and souls. This emotional cauldron was being seen for what it always had been – a complex problem.

What followed can only be described as one of the most bizarre three months in British political history. Indicative votes came and went, a prime minister resigned, parliament was prorogued, parliament was reinstated, the conversations between prime minister and monarch were questioned and chaos reigned supreme. A country once proud of its democratic processes had reached an unfathomable depth of political nonsense.

While the farcical stalemate played itself out, the political time bomb was ticking. The complex had become chaotic, and when there is chaos, decisive action is required. The resultant general election produced a landslide victory for a political organisation whose manifesto had minimal content, but its message was consistent, emotionally charged and framed around resolution.

The reason for highlighting this is that while communities can be restricted by borders and boundaries, they are made up of only one thing, and that is people. This is what makes them complex. Common sense or financial security are important considerations, but so often they will not be the primary drivers of a community.

Whether you are building a community or integrating into one, it is essential to appreciate the human element. In the same way that a leader is encouraged to create a trusting relationship with colleagues at work, take the time to understand the history, the characters and the context of your community. It is a worthwhile investment if you want to become a part of it.

Community architecture

A choir is a community. It's a combination of people who have a shared interest, in this case a group of singers who can make beautiful music and provide joy to both themselves and others. To reduce the risk of musical mayhem, a conductor ensures that the singers have not only a clear grasp of the music, but more importantly, an appreciation of how they will work together. Whether synchronising the sopranos or tempering the tenors, the conductor will be the person who consciously designs, advises and facilitates the harmony, both in music and persona. Without the cohesive power of the baton, despite every good intention, the choir runs the risk of producing a discordant dirge. In this respect, the conductor is a great example of a community architect.

Usually associated with building, the word architect also has relevance when we're thinking about both the creation of, and interaction with, a community. In the world of bricks and mortar, the architect can provide a spark of imagination and a vision on paper (or these days, a clever piece of software), and be the creator of a functional building. Sometimes, the process starts from scratch; at other times, it will involve the adaptation of a pre-existing structure. Whether it be genesis, development or redesign, the community architect does a similar job, though this time the integration is not between bricks and mortar, it is between people.

If we further break down the process of architecture, the analogy becomes even stronger. A building project often starts with a dream. Conjured up in the heart, it is something that brims with enthusiasm and promise, but will be short on detail. The initial job of the architect is to explore, refine and create some sense out of the vision. As ideas shift from the mind, the architect produces drawings, adding annotations as they sketch out the early signs of reality.

At this point, energy and enthusiasm are high and momentum is gathering pace, but this is the time when the good architect will pause. Before considering any of the detail, they need to test the vision, sound out objections, understand the consensus and identify the key supporters and antagonists. If there are dissenters, the architect will listen to them and evaluate their concerns, looking to understand the reason for the challenge. Is it based on practicality, competition, emotional history, prejudice or simply fear of change? Whatever the push back, empathy and putting themselves in the mind of the objector tends to be a more effective and cheaper strategy for the architect than rapidly dismissing the thoughts of others. After all, those people were not in the architect's head when they conjured up the dream.

The same principle is true for the community architect. Your idea may well be a great one, but have you explored and thought through not just the technical objections, but those of a more animate nature? Have you created a moment to seek the opinion of and talk ideas through with friends, family and other interested parties rather than ploughing on single-mindedly with obsessive abandon? This is an essential investment of time before heading on to the next stage of the community build.

Once the architect has addressed the challenges and gained support for their ideas, it is time for them to work on more comprehensive plans. They map out materials, budgets and timeframes; these are all important tasks if the architect is to transform their vision into a detailed document that will satisfy the scrutiny of the arbitrators who will determine whether the project can proceed.

While a community architect may not need to sit before a formal panel, somewhere on the journey it is likely that you will have questions asked of you. If you can give detailed answers, it will demonstrate clarity and depth of thinking and affirm that your vision is more than just a whim and a fancy.

Once everyone has reached a consensus and your dream has been given the green light, it will be time to start the building work. For a house build, this is when holes are dug, bricks laid, pipes plumbed, electrics installed, fixtures and fittings positioned.

If only it was that simple – rarely does a build go without a snag! The digging of foundations may be challenged by the appearance of a previously uncharted drain; the scaffolder you were planning to use may have gone into liquidation; the neighbours may be hell-bent on making things difficult. While the process of creation may have seemed straightforward, in many cases, the reality is far from it and the catalogue of glitches can be long and tiresome.

The community architect will have hurdles to overcome, too, with personalities, politics, purse strings and practicalities all having the potential to create headaches. In the same way that the builder must adapt in challenging times, the community architect has to be agile and adeptly navigate the barriers that are placed before them.

The final step in the architect's journey is the process of signing off. Inspectors examine the work and issue certificates, and finally the building will be handed over to those who will use it. For the community architect, the story is slightly different. Typically, you will want to be part of your creation rather than passing everything over to someone else and disappearing off into the sunset. It can be tough to loosen your grip on something that you conceived in your heart and soul and developed with emotional blood, sweat and tears. But at some point, for the legacy of the project, you as the community architect have to let go of the steering wheel and become part of a symbiotic environment where people feed off each other and the collective flourishes together.

Now that you know what a community is and how to build one, what can possibly go wrong? Forewarned is forearmed, so in the next chapter, we will have a look at some typical barriers to the success of your community and how to overcome them.

8
Dismantling Barriers

Communities of people are complex in nature and can be destabilised by a whole host of things, but two of the more common barriers can be the inability to harness people of different ages and an inability to think laterally. These factors seem to cause so many headaches to so many communities, it may be worth thinking about your approach to both generational angst and what is sometimes referred to as 'the problem space' if you want to increase the power of the many.

Generational angst

Whether it be our work colleagues or our local neighbourhood, a community is made up of people with a wide range of ages. As our attitudes and interactions with life tend to be shaped by generational traits, age-induced differences can often be a trigger for angst that builds barriers and breaks down lines of communication. Instead of integrating knowledge from across the generational spectrum, we create an environment punctuated by misunderstanding, suspicion and intolerance.

It can be useful to understand the typical defining traits of each generation. As with all stereotypes, these are purely a guide; for example, some people's individual traits are defined more by parental influence rather than date of birth.

Traditionalists are people born before 1945, so while there may not be many of these people left in the workplace, their influence lives on and can still be seen. They were heavily impacted by the Second World War, so unsurprisingly, they thrive on discipline, respect seniority and yearn for security. Many would have kept one job for the whole of their career and they are quite happy to be rewarded in a dignified and subtle manner rather than a fanfare of praise. The traditionalists simply do not require this, and would consider it an embarrassment.

Traditionalists worked in a time when technology, certainly compared to today's standard, was minimal, meaning that the boundary between life at work and life away from it was much more clearly defined. Yes, there was a time when people really did only work from nine to five.

Baby Boomers were born between 1946 and 1964. As the world opened up for business in the late 1970s and 1980s and entrepreneurial spirit was encouraged, this generation became aware that fame and wealth were not just a possibility for the titled. They lived to work, and the underlying belief was the more you did, the more money you would get. The sixty-plus-hour week was invented, and a wider distribution of wealth followed.

Work was a dominant force, and for many, it was also a significant part of their social life. Any additional interaction with their local community was at best superficial. Work-life balance was non-existent, relationships suffered and divorce rates went up.

Generation X were born between 1965 and 1980. These people are the pioneers and incubators of the technological revolution. They were driven by learning and invention, having found themselves in an emerging workplace where the leadership was no longer dictated by title or age; and moreso the ability to imagine and invent.

The challenges of parental splits made Generation X aware that there was more to life than just work, and the topic of work-life balance started to creep into conversations. This generation was still happy to work long hours, but in addition to financial reward, they wanted to be compensated with time off, so the concept of time in lieu became more widespread.

Millennials were born between 1981 and 1996. Tech-savvy, community-spirited and transient, these people decided not to let work dominate their lives and they shaped the concept of work-life integration. With short-term contracts resulting in the absence of financial security, they sought a positive work environment that provided them with other benefits. And they achieved status through a new form of currency – peer judgement and in particular digital likes and followers.

Generation Z were born post-1997. These people are not just tech-savvy, they are tech fluent. Their lives away from work are typically dominated by the connectivity that their phone provides. Old-fashioned dating is a thing of the past as relationships are burgeoned through a filtration process of swiping right or left, and entertainment, shopping and creativity are accessible twenty-four hours a day. Work is now the place for human interaction. People come to the office to have their breakfast, clubs are set up that might revolve around learning a language or playing a sport. The office is now a centre for social support.

With so much variation in outlooks, it is hardly surprising that angst sometimes arises between the generations. Take, for example, the attitudes towards health, in particular the relationship between health and the workplace. The Traditionalist will think there is no link and will insist that their health is 'my business alone'. The Baby Boomer simply worked, so health was very much a secondary issue. They may have been introduced to the company medical and had a check-up every couple of years, but many saw this as a tokenistic perk that was of little relevance to them.

Those in Generation X started to see the detrimental effects of long hours, and at this point workplaces encouraged a more proactive approach to health. Schemes such as subsidised gym membership were introduced and complemented by a more consistent approach to occupational health and safety.

For Millennials, health is important. They are happy to talk about things that impact them physically and mentally; they respect diversity and may even set up a special interest group or club to provide a community of support.

Generation Z are likely to get their medical support and input through their mobile devices. For them health is not just a topic but also a service that is readily accessible through the press of a button.

Attitudes through the generations have shifted from the hierarchical to the communal, but appreciation of the differing attitudes remains in the dark ages. If we do not understand folk, then we do not gel with them, we become impatient and progress can be thwarted.

We are diverse in many ways, but one way that is often poorly addressed is the variation in socioeconomic factors we were exposed to during our formative years. A range of events such as World War 2, globalisation of economies, the creation of the world-wide web, mobile technology, a new millennium and the attacks on the World Trade Center undoubtedly left their imprint and moulded traits.

However, it is not just major world events that define an age. As the Millennials found their way into the world of work, they were given the tag of being the 'snowflake generation'. The perception of older generations was that Millennials had life 'too easy' – no war, no miners' strikes, no civil unrest, and with luxuries such as travel and mobile phones becoming the social norm, Millennials were regarded as the generation that lacked commitment and flitted its way through life.

Maybe some of that is true, but the Millennials are also the generation that has been exposed to zero-hour contracts and apprentice schemes designed to provide an excellent grounding for a future career, that have in many cases over-promised, under-delivered and simply been used to provide low-cost labour. The saying 'you reap what you sow' springs to mind, and it is hardly surprising that the lack of commitment shown by organisations may be mirrored by the Millennial.

We have concentrated on the angst caused by generational differences, but it may be worth thinking about how you address diversity in general. Wouldn't it be better to encourage an understanding and tolerance of all? An environment where competencies and preferences are acknowledged and the best bits blended to create a cohesive community? One where the technophile helps the technophobe, and the politically astute mentors the enthusiasm of youth. Whether it is race, religion, colour, gender, sexuality or any other classification of diversity, I challenge you to think about how you can build bridges.

I like to think of this as building bridges. If you are going to win with your community, it is likely that you will need to walk over a bridge.

Intellectual inertia

Every so often, I am asked to talk to final-year physiotherapy students. It is a session that covers what I have got up to over the past thirty years, aims to inspire and has three key messages:

- Push your boundaries to where you want them to go.

- Avoid creating 'what if' moments.

- The importance of looking through windows.

The last point is worth highlighting. When I first qualified, I would always be looking into the window of physiotherapy. I believed that if I looked hard enough, if I wormed my way through the textbooks, I would find the answer, but there were times when I ended up stumped. It took me a few years to understand that sometimes you have to look out of the window.

The moment I accepted the limitations of looking in and started, on occasion, to look out of the window was a career-defining lightbulb moment. I was able to see a broader landscape. I am sure this moment occurs in other professions too.

EXAMPLE – MADERO ESTE

I was introduced to a great story that encapsulates this concept by the marketing expert and author of *The Contagious Commandments* Paul Kemp-Robertson, when he talked me through the creation of Madero Este in Argentina.

Situated on the eastern side of Buenos Aires, Madero Este is a complex of shops, accommodation and restaurants that sprang out of an old industrial area. As the state-of-the-art facilities were developed, space needed to be sold; Madero Este would only be deemed a success if populated, and marketeers were engaged to create a campaign that would drive awareness and be a magnet to the masses.

While I am sure that the creative director in charge of pulling together the plan used a whole host of marketing metrics, analytics and theory, he was also prepared to look out of the window. He placed himself firmly in the shoes and mind of the consumer, and soon discovered that for all the billboards, TV advertisements, special offers or opening spectaculars, there was a challenge. While sited a little over a quarter of a mile from the hustle and bustle of city life, Madero Este was incredibly close to downtown Buenos Aires, as the crow flies, however the quarter-mile divide was filled with an expanse of water. To reach the shining lights, people were going to have to make a circuitous journey so tortuous that even the most committed shopaholic would be put off.

This was a critical finding. When the agency reported back to the owners, they didn't present a paraphernalia of advertising bling. Instead, the suggestion was simple – spend money on building a bridge over the River Plate. And despite the cost being 50% more than the initial marketing budget, that is exactly what followed.

The Puente de la Mujer is not only a piece of architecture that now provides a connection across the 170-metre divide between pedestrian and product, it is now considered a tourist attraction in its own right.

This is a great story of how a marketeer was happy to abandon their professional skillset and look out of the window to find a solution. For all the marketing in all the world, failure was inevitable without this missing link. They had explored and discovered the problem space.

Sometimes the community architect will have to look out of their window too. Your vision for the future, one that was created weeks, months, maybe even years ago, can become so entrenched that you can't see the wood for the trees. You may need to accept a different perspective, and loosen the emotional attachment that sits between you and 'your baby'.

I have highlighted the importance of looking both in and out of a window, but there is another pane of glass that you may need to use, and that is a mirror. Examining how you sit within a problem involves matching what is needed with what you can offer. This can be a conversation that is hard to have with yourself, so it is best done with a trusted confidante.

Frank conversations with friends and associates can be hard to have and often fail to get to the crux of the matter. To avoid this, it is worth finding 'the mismatches'.

EXAMPLE – MY MISMATCHES

In this example, Person A is the one who is struggling, and Person B is the confidante. Both parties will need a template, as shown below. The themes for scoring can vary, but they need to be the same for both templates.

For each competency, both people will independently provide a score that reflects the importance of the topic. Before sharing their input with each other, they will use a different coloured pen and, on the same lines, provide a score for the skills that are in place to deliver each of the competencies. Person A will be scoring their own skills; Person B will be evaluating Person A.

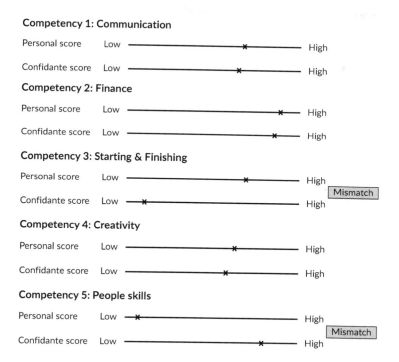

Competency 1: Communication

Personal score — Low ——————×———— High

Confidante score — Low ——————×———— High

Competency 2: Finance

Personal score — Low ——————————×— High

Confidante score — Low ———————————×— High

Competency 3: Starting & Finishing

Personal score — Low ——————————×— High

Confidante score — Low —×———————— High Mismatch

Competency 4: Creativity

Personal score — Low ——————————×——— High

Confidante score — Low ——————————×——— High

Competency 5: People skills

Personal score — Low —×—————————— High

Confidante score — Low ———————————×— High Mismatch

Once they have done this, Persons A and B compare notes and discuss the mismatches, ensuring there is time to explore these using intellectual, emotional and adaptive thinking. The first will offer insight; the emotional thinking will address relationships, collaboration and coalitions; while the adaptive provides a stimulus for invention and fluidity.

The different domains of thinking are essential when talking through a problem, but it is the bravery to hold up the mirror that so often is the catalyst for a discussion that can reignite passion and progress.

This brings section four to a close. What you do with your community is up to you, what they do with you is up to them, but rest assured what you do together may be some of the most enjoyable times of your life.

Conclusion

The challenge at the start of this book was to get you to think about your *Battle For Balance*. What game do you want to play? Which goals are you going to focus on? How are you going to turn changes into habits? Why bother? The narrative that followed these questions is not a prescription for life. Rather, it is a range of ideas that may be the stimulus you need if you are looking to find some answers and are intrigued by the thought of winning the game of life, three goals to nil, and ultimately creating a sense of balance.

I hope that you have been encouraged to think about the benefit of being proactive. Rather than continually reacting to problems, what are you doing to pre-empt them and futureproof yourself, your business and your personal world?

The simple visual analogue scale below shows the importance of what I call 'moving to the right'. Too often, people think that success is a matter of avoiding a slip to the left – in the world of health, this is known as prevention. I challenge you to focus on promotion.

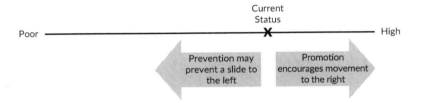

Sample visual analogue scale

While I have used health as the example here, the model is equally relevant if you're exploring energy, happiness, mindset, relationships, even business.

Aaron Antonovsky, a champion for the development of a proactive approach to health, developed the concept of salutogenesis in the late 1970s.[19] His view was that there are three characteristics that are required for human progression. First, a person needs to make sense of an action, and this needs to be accompanied by a belief that they can positively influence things. This is known as comprehensibility. Second, they will need to acknowledge the resources they require to ensure that their planned actions are realistic – manageability. Third, they will have clarity over why they are engaging with it – meaningfulness.

---

19   Aaron Antonovsky, *Health, Stress, and Coping* (Jossey Bass, 1979)

You don't need to remember the intricacies of salutogenesis as I have massively simplified a philosophical stance that is highly complex, but a lack of comprehensibility can lead to vagueness, a shortfall in manageability often results in frustration, and an absence of meaningfulness, despite every good intention, could easily end in failure.

Before finishing a book that encourages you to think about balance, it would be remiss of me not to mention the Japanese concept of *ikigai*, a 'reason for being'. This notion is imbued with a sense of meaning and completeness. Typically, it is demonstrated using four rings that fit together like a Venn diagram and it evaluates four dimensions of living. I have modified the Venn diagram approach below.

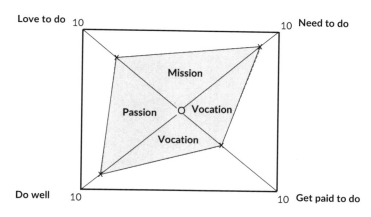

Sample ikigai *diagram*

Simply score yourself on each of the four scales (ten is positive and zero negative), join the crosses and colour in the central box. The unshaded area will demonstrate where you may be lacking when it comes to mission, vocation, profession and passion.

Ikigai may feel like a rather 'untouchable' phenomenon, but it is a useful concept that can help you understand how fulfilled your life is. As with the other scoring systems in this book, take the exercise a stage further by writing down the factors that have influenced your scores. It is always the story that influences the numbers.

Do remember that life changes around you and you change within it. What is right for you today may be totally wrong tomorrow. Your current recipe for success may not be the correct prescription for life in its entirety. To stay balanced, you will regularly need to make the time to pause, recognise where you are at, reflect on why you are there and reset before continuing on your journey.

Finally, it should be acknowledged that the word 'winning' can imply that someone else is losing. In a sporting contest, this may be true, but it is not necessarily correct in every walk of life. By looking at your wellbeing, your work and your world, you have the potential for three wins that are unlikely to result in another person being defeated. If you get things right, it is highly likely that many others will be winning, too.

Go well, live well, be well, and create some balance in your life.

Further Reading

The arena of self-help is heavily populated, but these books are my personal top ten. They have all positively influenced me and may be of interest to you, too.

Arden, P, *It's Not How Good You Are, It's How Good You Want to Be* (Phaidon Press, 2003). Short, sharp and to the point, this book highlights a host of behaviours that will prompt progression.

Coates, J, *The Hour Between Dog and Wolf: Risk-taking, gut feelings and the biology of boom and bust* (Fourth Estate, 2012). The author has enjoyed a varied career, from trading the global markets to becoming a research fellow at Cambridge University. His commentary on neuroscience, risk and decision making is fascinating.

Gawande, A, *Being Mortal: Illness, medicine and what matters in the end* (Portfolio Books Ltd, 2015). This book helps us to reconcile the fact that we will all disappear at some point and champions the importance of connectivity with ourselves, our community and the things that make us smile on the inside.

Hughes, D, *The Barcelona Way: Unlocking the DNA of a winning culture* (Macmillan, 2018). This book uses the story of FC Barcelona to demonstrate the importance of culture and authenticity and how these factors are required for effective leadership.

Jackson, P, *Eleven Rings* (Virgin Books, 2015). An autobiography from a talented basketball player, an extraordinary coach and a person who brought not only trophies to multiple franchises, but a sense of calm to a sport that often resembles a circus.

May, A, *Flip the Switch* (Messenger Publishing, 2007). This book is a straightforward look at a whole host of factors that influence health, wellbeing and performance. It is presented in a way that will inspire you, to make a plan for you.

Pearman, RR and Albritton, SC, *I'm Not Crazy, I'm Just Not You: The real meaning of the 16 personality types* (Nicholas Brealey Publishing, 2010). This book explores and explains personality and will help you understand both yourself and other people.

Quinn, A, *How to Be an Extraordinary Athlete: The secrets to sporting success* (Quintessential Publishing, 2012). A comprehensive look at the ingredients that can turn good sportspeople into great ones – many of the messages are relevant for the general population, too.

Swart, T, *The Source: Open your mind, change your life* (Vermilion, 2020). Penned by one of the world's most respected neuroscientists, this book helps us make sense of the two-way interaction between our brain and our behaviour.

Walker, M, *Why We Sleep: The new science of sleep and dreams* (Penguin, 2018). This book does what it says on the tin. It also provides an in-depth, yet digestible, insight into how we can all sleep a bit better.

Acknowledgements

I have been incredibly fortunate to work with people pretty much every day of my career, so this could have been a very long list. As a physiotherapist working in a clinic, I've examined twisted ankles and crooked spines. Patients trusted me with their bodies, but they were probably not so aware that they were also trusting me with their thoughts and feelings. They opened up about life, as it was often this that they really wanted fixing. While that was not within my remit or training, it was important for me to appreciate the complexities that people encounter and I have learned so much from my patients – so thank you all!

Christ's Hospital is a school that taught me many things, but the most powerful lesson was gratitude. Founded in 1557, it is a place of charity and tradition.

One of the rituals is a chapel service, held on the last day of the school year, where those leaving the establishment are challenged with a statement from the head teacher. The first sentence reads: 'I charge you never to forget the great benefits you have received in this place and, in time to come, according to your means, to do all that you can to enable others to enjoy the same advantage.' These words have had a strong influence on me. I have not forgotten and am incredibly grateful for the care I was given.

Lord's Cricket Ground is a special place, and since 1991, I have had the privilege of working with both Middlesex CCC and Marylebone CC. I am grateful to the players who've allowed me to sit in the inner sanctum of a dressing room and observe how teams can flourish and function – you have made me laugh and sometimes cry, but I am in awe of your sporting ability.

I have experienced support from many other people in the world of cricket, but I would specifically like to acknowledge John Jameson, Debbie Moore, Mike Gatting, John Emburey, Angus Fraser and the now sadly departed Frank Horan and Don Bennett for their trust and unequivocal decency as people.

As a leader of a small business, I employed many people over the years. Every single one of them has helped me learn, and while one or two may have contributed to my receding hairline, they have all stimulated the grey matter. Thank you one and all.

As for Optima-life, I am grateful to everyone who has helped the organisation develop. Setting up a business at a time of global recession was tough, introducing new technology, thinking and language was hard, but I received a lot of support on the journey. From fellow pioneers Tim Wright and Nigel Stockill to colleagues at Firstbeat Technologies, particularly Joni Kettunen and Tiina Hoffman, I can assure you all, it is appreciated.

Professionally, there are numerous people who have supported me for long periods of my working life, particularly Maggie McNerney, Sue Henry, Mike Farrar, Catherine Loftus and Karen Middleton. I can only thank them for their time and encouragement. Equally, there are a couple of people who have significantly influenced my thinking. John Buchanan opened my mind to a new way of leadership and Andrew May's book *Flip the Switch* stimulated a new way of living.

To the members, friends and family of Garden Fields Dads Cricket Club – you are all bonkers, but together we have learned so much about community being, and occasionally you make me smile! In particular, a big thank you to Amy and Robyn West who allowed me to tell a small bit of their story.

Thank you to my children Alice and Kit – you fill me with pride, amaze me with your character and constantly make me beam. I just need to get better at showing it.

And finally, the biggest thank you of all goes to my darling wife, Tracy. Aside from putting up with me for well over a quarter of a century, she has done so much. Her support is immeasurable, her trust unsurmountable, and more than anything, I thank her for unlocking my soul.

The Author

Simon Shepard is part of a select group of people who have direct experience of working within the sectors of sport, health and business. He has a desire to be ahead of the curve through constantly challenging the status quo. He's an entrepreneur and, if the truth be told, a bit of a nuisance.

Having qualified as a Chartered Physiotherapist in 1988, he spent two years working in both the NHS and the private sector before being appointed sole physiotherapist at Lord's Cricket Ground where he looked after the playing staff of both Middlesex County Cricket Club and Marylebone Cricket Club for over a decade. He subsequently oversaw the growth of a sports medicine and science department that now brings together a range of professionals and became one of the first recipients of gold level accreditation by The Association of Chartered Physiotherapists in Sports Medicine.

In 1992, Simon set up Central Health, a physiotherapy practice based in central London. With the development of innovative partnership models, the business flourished and grew from a one-man band to an organisation that employed over fifty therapists. In 2007, on realising his job was done, he successfully exited.

With an increasing interest in the links between health and performance, and the emergence of technology that can objectively measure stress, sleep and lifestyle, he founded Optima-life in 2007. Initially, the focus was solely on technology, but Simon soon realised the benefit of blending data with training and developed programmes that have been delivered to a range of organisations in multiple continents. The business has a particular emphasis on supporting healthcare workers, and this was recognised when Optima-life earned a Medilink Award for Partnership with the NHS.

And as for the tag of being a nuisance, Simon can take what is traditionally thought of as a 'fluffy topic' and make it distinctly uncomfortable, whether it be through the collection of physiological data or his reputation for asking tough questions. He may well get under your skin, but more than anything, he encourages *you* to get under *yours*.

🌐 www.optima-life.com

in www.linkedin.com/in/simon-shepard-a9868a16

🐦 @OptimaLife

Printed in Great Britain
by Amazon

70225468R00106